THE BASICS OF

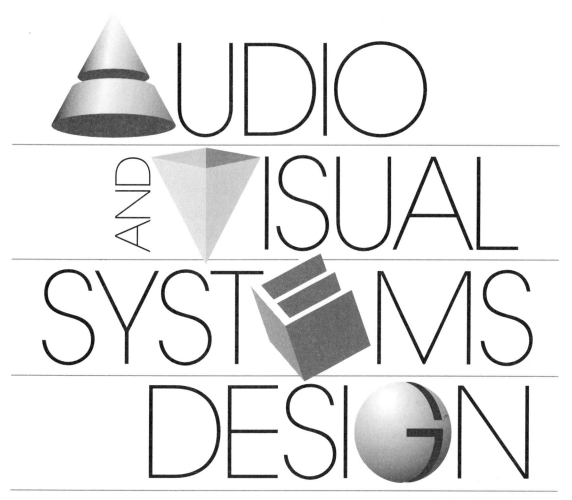

AUDIO AND VISUAL SYSTEMS DESIGN

Revised Edition

infoComm

INTERNATIONAL COMMUNICATIONS
INDUSTRIES ASSOCIATION, INC.®

The Basics of Audio and Visual Systems Design: Revised Edition

Published by the International Communications Industries Association, Inc. (ICIA)®
11242 Waples Mill Road, Fairfax, VA 22030, www.infocomm.org

Edited by Mike Weems, CTS, MCP

Cover design by Scott Hansbarger
Book design by Cristina Diez de Medina, A Scribbler's Press, Ltd.
Copyediting by Wendy A. Jordan

Copyright 2003 by the International Communications Industries Association, Inc.®
First printing 2003
Second printing 2005

Printed in the United States of America
Library of Congress Control Number 2003105705
ISBN 0-939718-19-7

In the last 20 years audiovisual professionals may not have known they were being selected for advancement in their company when their supervisor told them, "Here, read this book." Many of them today, however, credit *The Basics of Audio and Visual Systems Design* as their first and most important introduction to being an AV professional. It is for that reason that the International Communications Industries Association, Inc.® (ICIA) has undertaken the task of producing a second edition that will replace the tattered copies on the industry's bookshelves and introduce a whole new generation to the field.

Prior to 1983, when this work was first published by the National Audio-Visual Association, Inc. (NAVA), renamed the ICIA that same year, no one book contained the diverse set of physics, electronics, ergonomics and design that makes up the audiovisual industry. Ray Wadsworth, by collecting all of these topics in one place, provided the audiovisual industry its own, unique identity for the first time. He, along with other pioneering writers, began to codify the knowledge of practitioners and in so doing made it possible for the next generation to build on their knowledge. Today, as ICIA presents this book to the industry, it owes much to Ray Wadsworth's foresight in capturing the elements that make up an industry that is both technical and creative.

Through the years, *The Basics of Audio and Visual Systems Design* has served as a primary resource for ICIA's Design School. The first Design classroom courses were delivered in 1997. They have evolved into today's robust combination of online courses, multiple-day classroom sessions, seminars and workshops at InfoComm exhibitions around the world, as well as certification opportunities. The curriculum committee that developed these courses, and the outstanding facilitation provided by Steve Thorburn, PE, CTS-D, CTS-I, and John Campanella, CTS-D, through the years, have set the industry standard in education of the audiovisual design community. Steve, John and the editors and writers of this book have expanded it beyond the basics of the 1983 edition and educated an ever-expanding group of design professionals that long will long serve our industry, our members, and our customers.

The second edition was undertaken by The Professional Education and Training Committee (PETC) of ICIA and spearheaded in its initial phases by Fred Dixon, CTS, of Dixon Media Systems and Design and Kim Milliken of Da-Lite Screen Company. Mike Weems, CTS, MCP, of InFocus Corporation, built upon their work and brought the project to completion. We owe all three and their companies a debt of gratitude.

Although the science and technology that are the foundation of the audiovisual industry haven't changed, today's applications provide a power to ideas never dreamed of in 1983. It is ICIA's privilege to provide this work to a new generation of audiovisual professionals, with gratitude to those who came before.

Randal A. Lemke, Ph.D.
Executive Director
International Communications
Industries Association, Inc.

ICIA owes much to Ray Wadsworth's foresight in capturing the elements that make up an industry that is both technical and creative.

Preface

In 1983 Raymond Wadsworth, PE, wrote the first edition of this book. It was a monumental task to assemble in one place the many elements that audiovisual systems design at that time comprised. His work was widely heralded, and the book became the "AV bible" that many in the audiovisual industry refer to even today.

But audiovisual systems have advanced considerably since 1983, so in January of 2001 Kim Milliken, with Da-Lite Screens, took up the task of editing a revised and updated version of the book. At a meeting that month during ICIA's Institute for Professional Development in San Antonio, Texas, Kim enlisted a group of individuals to assist him in the task of revision and, in some cases, writing entire new chapters. Work began.

The initial goal of Kim and all of the section editors/writers was to update the book while remaining as faithful to the original as possible.

A short time later, Kim was diagnosed with what proved to be a terminal illness. He set the book project aside, and later was forced to give it up entirely. Finally, in the summer of 2002, I realized that if the book were going to get published, it would have to be without Kim as the editor. Kim had served as my Vice Chair of the Professional Education and Training Committee (PETC) until that time. After finding no one else to volunteer, I assumed the role of editor.

A few of the original section contributors had completed their tasks; other sections had not even been begun. In a reorganization and expansion of Ray's book, Kim had outlined 13 sections. Of these, Kim had tackled seven himself, covering projection screens, optics and light. Later it was decided to combine some of Kim's material, resulting in a total of 12 sections.

The original and new material is a treasure trove of knowledge about our industry. However, I immediately found that editing what amounts to a technical reference book is challenging indeed. I found that the most difficult task in editing a "basics" book is deciding what to put in and what to leave out. I hope that what we have compiled will satisfy your needs. The staff at ICIA, all of the contributors and I welcome your comments and suggestions. In fact, we hope that the task of revising this book will be an ongoing one, with more editions to come as the industry advances. Each section of this book has been reviewed numerous times. But as you use this work, you might happen upon some mistake that we missed. If you do, please drop ICIA a line.

My other task was to update the look of the book. The layout has changed from two columns to one, new fonts have been adopted, all drawings, tables, figures and charts are new or "refreshed," and more open space has been provided for notes. Even the cover retains elements from the old, while projecting a more modern image.

Many individuals contributed to this book; they are listed on the acknowledgments page. Since ICIA is a member organization, the members who assisted with the editing and writing of this book did so as volunteers, without compensation. The countless hours, thoughts and ideas they contributed have been invaluable, and we thank them.

What Ray and Kim wrought (with a little tinkering by us mortals) has finally made it back onto the shelves again. I hope they are pleased.

Mike Weems, CTS, MCP
Chair, Professional Education and Training Committee
International Communications
Industries Association, Inc.

What Ray and Kim wrought (with a little tinkering by us mortals) has finally made it back onto the shelves again.

This book is dedicated to
two of the true legends of our industry.

Raymond H. Wadsworth, PE

At InfoComm 2001:
ICIA President
Spencer Bullins, CTS,
presents Ray Wadsworth,
original author of
*The Basics of Audio and
Visual Systems Design*,
proposed cover of
revised book.

The late Raymond H. Wadsworth, PE, was Senior Vice-president for Hubert Wilke, Inc., communications facilities consultants. For nine years, prior to joining the Wilke organization in 1965, he was Director of Engineering and Product Development for TelePrompTer Corporation and TelePro Industries. During that time he supervised design and engineering for more than 100 audiovisual system installations, including the Air Force Command Post, Joint Chiefs of Staff in the Pentagon, National Aeronautics and Space Administration, White Sands Missile Range, Johnson & Johnson, Consolidated Edison, Phillips Petroleum Company, Princeton University, the University of Illinois, and Orange Coast College.

He received his mechanical engineering degree from Duke University and his professional engineer's license from the University of the State of New York. He was co-author of an architectural textbook and wrote extensively for such magazines as *Machine Design*, *Architectural Record*, *American School and University* and *Video Systems*.

He was the sole author of the first edition of this book in 1983.

M. K. Milliken

Kim Milliken was one of the founders of Optixx Screen Systems (OSS), the first U.S. company to design and manufacture large size Fresnel/Lenticular screens. In 1991, OSS was acquired by Da-Lite Screen Company, and Kim became Director of Display Technology.

While at Da-Lite, he authored "Angles of View," a monthly series of technical papers on the various aspects of visual displays. He also advanced professional development in the audiovisual industry through teaching ICIA Design School Onsite and through the Attributes of Visual Display workshops at ICIA's annual trade show, InfoComm. Through his many years of service in leadership positions, as a member of the ICIA Board of Governors and of the Steering Committee for the Professional Education and Training Committee (PETC), Kim made an invaluable contribution to the profession and to ICIA.

In 2002, the ICIA Board of Governors honored Kim with the ICIA Distinguished Achievement Award. In 2003, the ICIA Professional Education and Training Committee (PETC) honored Kim posthumously with the Fred Dixon Service in Education Award.

Acknowledgments

Many people contributed to making this book possible. Please thank them for their efforts on our behalf.

We are grateful to the following individuals who were responsible for either editing a section, writing a new section or doing a combination of both. Except as noted, sections were originally written by Raymond H. Wadsworth, PE.

SECTION 1 was edited by Kim Milliken, with new material contributed by George Mihalakis, CEO, Gain Micro-Optics.

SECTION 2 was edited by Kim Milliken.

SECTION 3 was edited by Kim Milliken, with new material contributed by George Mihalakis, CEO, Gain Micro-Optics.

SECTION 4 was edited by Kim Milliken.

SECTION 5 was edited by Kim Milliken.

SECTION 6 was edited by Kim Milliken.

SECTION 7 was written by Jody Thomas, CTS, CEO, Kayye Consulting, Inc.

SECTION 8 was edited by Steve Thorburn, PE, CTS-D, CTS-I, co-founder, Thorburn Associates, Inc.

SECTION 9 was partially written by Ray H. Wadsworth, PE, and contains new material written and edited by Mike Weems, CTS, MCP, Senior Technical Trainer, InFocus Corporation.

SECTION 10 was written by Phillip Giddings, PE, founder of Engineering Harmonics, Inc.

SECTION 11 was written by L. William Nattress, III, Senior Associate, Shen Milsom and Wilke, Inc.

SECTION 12 was jointly written by Scott Sharer, CTS, Communication Design Group, and Jim Smith, CVE, AV Integration Support Engineer, Polycom.

Thanks go to the following peer reviewers who made corrections and/or additions to the various sections.

SECTION 1 was reviewed and edited by George Mihalakis, CEO, Gain Micro-Optics, and Judith D. Loughran, CTS, Senior Vice President, Da-Lite Screen Company.

SECTION 2 was reviewed by George Mihalakis, CEO, Gain Micro-Optics, and reviewed and edited by Judith D. Loughran, CTS, Senior Vice President, Da-Lite Screen Company.

SECTION 3 was reviewed and edited by George Mihalakis, CEO, Gain Micro-Optics, and Judith D. Loughran, CTS, Senior Vice President, Da-Lite Screen Company. (At George's suggestion, the original Sections 3 and 4 were merged.)

SECTION 4 was reviewed and edited by Judith D. Loughran, CTS, Senior Vice President, Da-Lite Screen Company.

SECTION 5 was reviewed and edited by Judith D. Loughran, CTS, Senior Vice President, Da-Lite Screen Company.

SECTION 6 was reviewed and edited by Judith D. Loughran, CTS, Senior Vice President, Da-Lite Screen Company.

SECTION 7 was reviewed by Steve Barlow, Product Marketing Manager–CDS, Philips Business Solutions, and Gary Kayye, CTS, Chief Visionary, Kayye Consulting.

SECTION 8 was reviewed by Raymond H. Wadsworth, PE.

SECTION 9 was reviewed by Christopher J. Soltesz, Broadcast Television Engineer, Sony Electronics, Inc.

SECTION 11 was reviewed by Billy Duncan, Technical Trainer, AMX Corp., and Dave Silberstein, CTS, Training Manager, Crestron Electronics, Inc.

SECTION 12 was jointly reviewed by the two section authors.

Additional Review

Additional gratitude is extended to Scott Walker, CTS-D, Principal, Waveguide Consulting, Inc., and Mark Valenti, President, The Sextant Group, for looking over the final product.

Members of the ICIA staff also contributed to this effort:

Randal A. Lemke, Ph.D., Executive Director

Terry Friesenborg, CTS, Senior Vice President of Education

Taly Walsh, Senior Vice President of Marketing and Membership

Melissa Taggart, Vice President of Education and Workforce Development

Catherine Zipf, Director of Marketing

Hector Rodriguez, CTS, Technical Support Manager

Finally, ICIA joins Mike Weems, CTS, MCP, Senior Technical Trainer, InFocus Corporation, in thanking InFocus for its generosity in giving him the time and materials to accomplish this task.

Contents

Figures, tables and charts *(con't)*

Section 8

Figures, tables and charts *(con't)*

THE PROJECTED

IMAGE FORMAT

edited by **M.K. MILLIKEN**

Kim Milliken, of Da-Lite Screen
Company and founder of Optixx
Screen Systems, spent more
than 25 years in the audiovisual
industry. He is best known for
his commitment to educating
the industry with a level of
intelligence and sophistication
that remains unparalleled.

The reason that virtually all projected image formats are wider than they are high presumably has to do with the configuration of our own eyes as a side-by-side pair. It seems a perfectly natural tendency for image content producers to want to frame a scene horizontally. Nevertheless, although the photographic process was well established previously, professional film widths and frame sizes were not standardized until the early 1900s when 35mm was accepted as the standard size in both the United States and Europe. Images were framed in an approximate 4:3 ratio of width to height, and this shape, adopted by the Academy of Motion Picture Arts and Sciences in 1927, became established as the "Academy" format. Each frame measured 0.825" wide by 0.600" high and spanned four sprocket holes on the film.

Another useful way to express this relationship between an image's width and height or, as is often said, its "aspect ratio," is to use a single number that is the quotient of the larger number divided by the smaller. Thus, 4:3 = 1.33, for example.

How TV images acquired their shape

Since 1.33 was the principal aspect ratio of the motion picture industry, the designers of early television in the 1940s realized that if their medium's aspect ratio was kept the same, they could broadcast movies without any significant loss in frame size.

It is also true that when the developers of commercial television decided that its bandwidth couldn't afford to be more than 6 MHz and that its vertical resolution had to be at least 525 lines, something very close to a 1.33 maximum screen width popped out of the calculations as a mandated default.

And finally, the squarer 1.33 aspect ratio worked well to minimize the TV medium's bandwidth and resolution disadvantage relative to film. Since image detail all but disappears in the coarseness of televised wide-shots, TV content typically is shot as sequences of multiple close-up and tight-shot cuts; that way subject detail still can be seen in the medium's lower resolution. This technique rewards the vertical, "portrait" aspect of the picture.

Other aspect ratios used in film

Notice that the 4:3 genesis had nothing to do with how visually pleasing images in this aspect ratio actually are. In fact there isn't anything intrinsically appealing about 4:3 pictures beyond atonement for television's limitations. That is why the movie industry, which at first regarded television as a major threat to its revenues, was quick to develop a whole series of wide, panoramic screen shapes including Cinerama® (2.76:l), CinemaScope® (2.35:l), 70mm (2.05:l) and the currently familiar Panavision® (1.85:1)—the prevalent "letterbox" ratio. Any of these wide-screen formats is a better approximation of the human visual field than the boxy, nearly square shape of a TV screen. Moreover, film's superior resolution and "landscape" aspect preserved subject detail in wide-shots and made possible the "two-shot" classic in film production, in which people speak to one another in the same frame. This technique was virtually nonexistent in TV content production.

Aspect ratios used with computers

Although computer-generated displays have gone through a long series of desktop resolution increases, with one exception their aspect ratio has remained 4:3. The exception, "Workstation" format, had an aspect ratio of 1,280:1,024 or 5:4 (1.25:1). This format was squarer than the 4:3 standard and originally was intended for engineering applications such as CAD/CAM. A less rectangular 5:4 aspect ratio was deemed more suitable for design work.

The aspect ratio for computer images was 4:3 for a simple reason: Their display technology already existed in that shape. Personal computers followed television by about 35 years, but the CRT (cathode ray tube) display screens providing the visual interfaces for these two markets were virtually identical (their differences being mostly electronic). Rather than heap the cost of redeveloping CRT production onto the fledgling computer industry, its pioneers made the proper choice of simply keeping with the 4:3 TV tube standard.

The HDTV format

To understand the thinking that went into development of HDTV (high definition television), we need to appreciate that its aspect ratio, 16:9, tells only half its story. The other half is the tale of its resolution.

U.S. television nominally has 525 lines of resolution (PAL, or Phase Alternate Line, system supports 625). To avoid seeing these raster lines, we're supposed to sit seven screen heights back from an NTSC (National Television System Committee) display. That suggests that the proper viewing distance for a 27" diagonal screen is about 9.5'. From the "seven screen heights" number we also can determine that the image we're watching will occupy only 10 degrees within our horizontal field of view.

Now let's look at the HDTV picture (Figure 1-1).

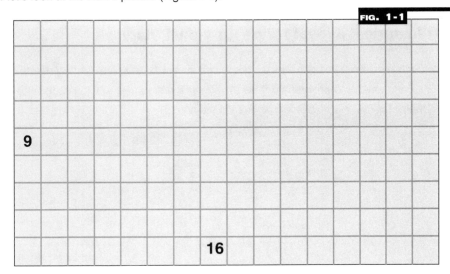

FIG. 1-1

16:9 aspect ratio

First of all, we notice that its aspect ratio has gotten much wider. 4:3 has jumped to 16:9 (in film nomenclature 1.33:1 has become 1.78:1). In addition it has twice as many lines vertically (1,080). This statistic is a little misleading because the overall resolution of HDTV is not two times better than NTSC; it's more than five times better. Video resolution is established by the total available pixels inside a display. That number is calculated by multiplying the vertical lines times the horizontal frequency. Hence, if there are just over 350,000 pixels on today's NTSC screens; there are just over 2 million on an HDTV display.

At that resolution in the 16:9 aspect ratio, how far back should a person sit? The answer is three screen heights. And at a viewing distance of 3 screen heights, the screen fills fully 33 degrees of our horizontal field-of-view.

These numbers are significant because the designers of HDTV appreciated "that a wider aspect ratio coupled with improved picture quality would provide the viewer far more involvement with the program. It was determined by exhaustive research and testing that a 30-degree field of vision would not only excite the central portion of the human visual system, but the peripheral vision as well, that gives a very heightened experience of reality to the viewer...."[1]

Other, independently conducted research showed that "the human visual system is clearly divided by two functions—the ability to see detail better in the central area and the ability to see motion in the peripheral.[2] Thus, if video were ever going to match the impact of movies, it needed, quite literally, to change its image.

16:9 displays in professional AV

As the confluence of the various projection media continues, the ultimate dominance of high resolution, 16:9 projection systems is certain. The major obstacle that exists as of this writing is the projector manufacturers' reluctance to make the commitment to hardware that can display 1,920 x 1,080 (or 1080i HDTV) native resolution. When that threshold is crossed, the superiority of 16:9 over 4:3 will be recognized universally.

However, it should be considered that, since the dominant force in the AV projector industry market continues to be its portable sector, and since this sector is linked closely to the portable computer market, the 16:9 HD format must first be adopted by the manufacturers of the computers feeding signals to the AV projectors. A projector that can display 1,920 x 1,080 is of no use to anyone unless this signal format can be provided easily.

Other historical aspect ratios for visual displays

In the history of projected images, various formats have evolved to serve differing needs in the instructional and entertainment arenas. Table 1-1 shows the parameters of these historical formats. Newer formats are covered in other sections.

TABLE 1-1 Film and slide formats

ASPECT FORMAT	APERTURE RATIO	APERTURE (INCHES)		IMAGE SIZE (FEET)	
		h	w	H	W
16-MM MOTION PICTURE	1.33	0.284	0.380	V ÷ 8	1.33H
16-MM CINEMASCOPE	2.66	0.284	0.380	V ÷ 8	2.66H
35-MM MOTION PICTURE	1.37	0.600	10.825	V ÷ 8	1.37H
35-MM WIDE SCREEN	1.85	0.446	0.825	V ÷ 6 TO V ÷ 8	1.85H
35-MM CINEMASCOPE	2.35	0.715	0.839	V ÷ 6 TO V ÷ 8	2.35H
70-MM WIDE SCREEN	2.21	0.868	1.913	V ÷ 6 TO V ÷8	2.21 H
8-MM MOTION PICTURE	1.33	0.129	0.172	V ÷ 8	1.33H
SUPER 8-MM M.P.	1.34	0.158	0.211	V ÷ 8	1.34H
35-MM FILM STRIP	1.32	0.668	0.885	V ÷ 8	1.32H
35-MM d.f. SLIDE (HOR)	1.48	0.902	1.34	V ÷ 8	1.48H
35-MM d.f. SLIDE (VERT)	0.68	1.34	0.902	V ÷ 5.4	0.68H
SUPER SLIDE	1.00	1.50	1.50	V ÷ 5.4	H
"INSTAMATIC" 126	1.00	1.04	1.04	V ÷ 5.4	H
110 CARTRIDGE	1.31	0.51	0.67	V ÷ 8	1 .31 H
31/4" x 4" "LANTERN SLIDE"	1.09	2..75	3.00	V ÷ 8	1.09H
3 1/4 " x 4" POLAROID SLIDE	1.36	2.40	126	V ÷ 8 -	1.16H
OVERHEAD TRANSPARENCY	VARIES	10" MAX	10" MAX	V ÷ 5.4	VARIES
OPAQUE PROJECTOR	VARIES	10" MAX	10" MAX	V ÷ 5.4	VARIES

h = Height of projected aperture, inches.
w = Width of projected aperture, inches.
V = Viewing distance, from rear corner viewer to diagonally opposite side of screen, feet.
H = Image height, feet.
W = Image width, feet.

The proper size of projection images

Aspect ratios other than 4:3 in projection images produce a new problem when historical methods are applied for properly sizing them.

A projected image is sized correctly when the most distant viewer can comfortably read characters, numerals and other symbols that have been prepared in accordance with proper graphic standards. It was once thought that the calculation of proper image size depended on some multiple of image width (henceforth referred to as "w"). Indeed, when every image under consideration had the same aspect ratio, a formula based on image width made perfect sense.

However, as available aspect ratios multiplied, it soon became clear that reliance on such a width-based system led to considerable ambiguity. After all, if, for example, we were to suppose that 6w was a reliable distance to our least favored viewer (hereinafter referred to as "LFV"), and, if, perchance, that were to be true for 4:3 displays, what would happen if we applied the same formula to a 16:9 image?

The reason this is so important is that the visual task imposed by the display upon its LFV is an increasingly complex one as the data density of the typical images expected to be resolved inexorably increases in direct proportion to the ever-escalating computer power generating it.

Once upon a time the LFV's visual task was confined to looking, but in today's era of alphanumeric data display, looking has been replaced by reading. As materials projected before us acquire more graphical content, our visual task will surpass the demands of reading and evolve to examining.

When we read, we have available to us numerous visual cues. We know, for Latin-root languages for instance, to direct our eyes to the upper left-hand corner of the display and begin to scan right. Our experience with reading is helpful when our eyes encounter spatial breaks or edges. For example, even if the projected word "profitability" is degraded by, say, a cluster of failed pixels so it appears to us as "profi   ilty", the chance of still being able to recognize the word is very high.

If, however, we are examining a projected image with graphical content, such as a schematic diagram, it is apparent immediately that we have virtually no visual cues as to what portion of the image we should view first. And should there be any artifacts within the image that mask or distort a portion of its content, our natural recognition skills will be of no help.

The rules, then, for sizing any sort of contemporary image always should be predicated upon the image's height (henceforth referred to as "h"). Experience throughout the 1990s has convinced most AV professionals that, while the classic, 8h multiple remains perfectly okay for video-based displays, 6h is a much more reliable number for data, and 4h should be the ideal for graphics displays.

---

[1] Dale Pripps, "Widescreen TV – The HDTV Story," *Widescreen Review* July-August 1993: 17.

[2] Dale Pripps, "Widescreen TV – The HDTV Story," *Widescreen Review* July-August 1993: 20.

2

SCREEN SIZE VERSUS

CEILING HEIGHT

edited by **M.K. MILLIKEN**

Kim Milliken, of Da-Lite Screen
Company and founder of Optixx
Screen Systems, spent more
than 25 years in the audiovisual
industry. He is best known for
his commitment to educating
the industry with a level of
intelligence and sophistication
that remains unparalleled.

FIG. 2-1

Once we have become convinced of the importance of size as a prerequisite of effective imagery, we almost certainly are going to bump our heads against the mechanical limitation of ceiling height. Neither architects nor builders, professionals whose top priorities quite understandably are economic, normally are sensitive to issues regarding adequate image height. Instead, the height of the room in which an AV display system is to be installed ranges from 8' to 9.5' in a typical commercial construction.

Taking the more generous of those two numbers, let's see what might be the maximum length of a room that can be served by a projected image displayed below a 9.5' ceiling.

Bottom of image should be at least 4'0" above floor to prevent excessive head interference

FIG. 2-2

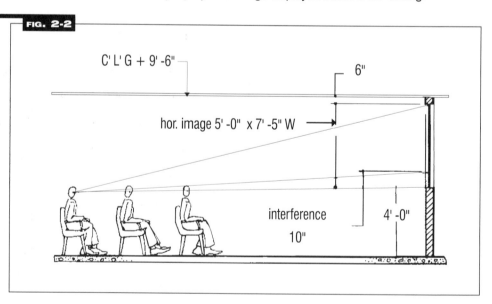

C' L' G + 9' -6"

6"

hor. image 5' -0" x 7' -5" W

interference 10"

4' -0"

Figure 2-2 shows that a viewer will experience about 10" of head interference when seated on a flat floor under the following conditions:

■ rows have staggered seats, so that the head of the person two rows in front of the viewer interferes;

■ rows are no closer than 36", chairback to chairback;

■ the bottom edge of the image is 48" above the finished floor.

Figure 2-3 shows that the height of the image cannot be more than 60" (allowing for 6" above the top of the image for proper aesthetics).

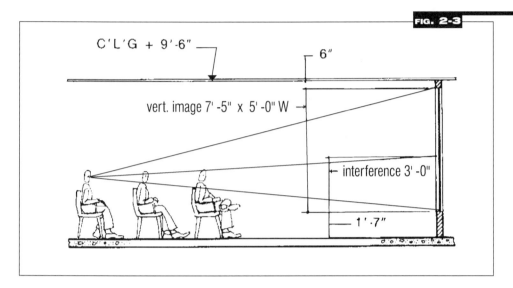

Image the size of that used horizontally in Figure 2-2 cannot be used vertically without excessive head interference

Following the formulas given at the end of Section 1, we find that the room can be 40' deep if the only thing to be watched is video, 30' deep if there is a data display, and a meager 20' deep if the display is graphical.

Since these dimensions are so restrictive, there seem to be only two effective ways to ease them: Get the architect and builder to raise the ceiling, or develop some workaround utilizing the software. Although this section can offer no guidance as to the accomplishment of the first option, it can provide some data useful in the second.

In the easiest and therefore simplest case, with respect to video nothing need be done. After all, watching video is primarily a recognition task. Therefore it is no great test of our visual acuity to be asked, even from great distance, whether the subject being imaged is a man or a woman.

With regard to data, however, more rigid standards exist. They rightfully concentrate on the smallest coherent element within the presented material. This, of course, is a single character, which becomes even more usefully defined as a lower case x.

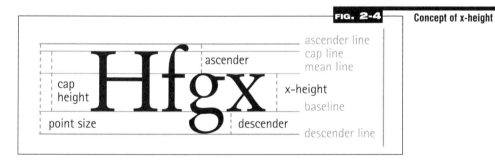

Concept of x-height

Figure 2-4 illustrates this concept of x-height. Using it we can establish ways to calculate its minimum dimensions so that it can be "read" reliably from any given viewing distance. Notice that we now are abandoning as useless any consideration of overall screen height and instead are concentrating on character height. This should give us considerably greater flexibility, even if the resultant mathematics are marginally more rigorous.

The way we can express the minimum requisite height of the lowercase letter x is to determine the number of degrees (just a scaleless way to say the amount of space, really) it must subtend on a viewer's retina to be recognizable as a lowercase x at any viewing distance.

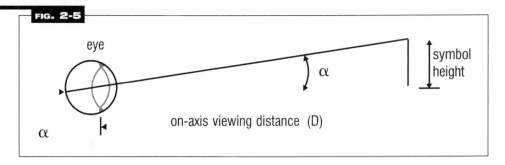

FIG. 2-5

As Figure 2-5 shows, it turns out that the minimum height (α) for the smallest symbol should subtend not less than 10 arc minutes. (An arc minute is a unit of angular measurement equal to one sixtieth of a degree, or 60 arc seconds.) What Table 2-1 also reveals, however, is that 10' is reliable only for viewers positioned nearly normal to the display.

Because all other viewers are obliged to look at the display, as it were, askance, their visual task is incrementally more demanding. The size of the symbols must be increased proportionately for them. Table 2-1 illustrates how symbol size must be increased as the viewing angle and display importance are increased.

TABLE 2-1   Symbol size vs. viewing angle as a reference

On-axis viewing distance (D)	Subtended Angle (in minutes of arc) (α)			
	10*	**16****	**20*****	
10 ft	0.35"	0.55"	0.70"	* Acceptable for non time-critical tasks
20 ft	0.70"	1.12"	1.40"	** Minimum standard when legibililty is important
30 ft	1.05"	1.67"	2.09"	*** 20-22 preferred for reading and colored symbols
40 ft	1.40"	2.24"	2.79"	

REQUIRED CHARACTER HEIGHT

The formulas for computing on- and off-axis viewing requirements are presented in Figure 2-6. Thus, even when we cannot make the screen large enough so that it is only a sixth or a fourth of the distance to its LFV (Least Favored Viewer), we can determine quite precisely the size at which the display's software must present its minimum character.

FIG. 2-6

General equations for subtended angle

On-axis viewing

$$\omega_1 = \frac{3438 \times \text{Symbol Height}}{\text{viewing distance*}}$$

Off-axis viewing

$$\omega_2 = \frac{\omega_1(\cos\alpha)^k}{\text{viewing distance*}}$$

ω = subtended angle in minutes of arc

α = off-axis angle

* = distance from viewer to screen along line-of-sight

Only rarely, if ever, will the equations given above yield an answer whose dimensions are predicated upon a viewer positioned in the audience's front row. This is justified, of course, because when the visual task is reading (rather than looking) no viewers are ever obliged to regard the entire screen at one time. Instead, viewers focus their attention on a sequential multitude of mini-screens that contain a word or small group of words. At any given instant, this is all that their eyes are obliged to focus on. In terms, then, of being comfortably able to resolve the contents of any of these "mini-screens," there is virtually no reasonable distance that can be defined as too close.

There is, however, an angular consideration that does limit a row's width. Its calculation involves determining how much geometric distortion can be tolerated within a projected image. By geometric distortion we mean the apparent deformation that occurs when our viewing angle to some portion of a display is anything other than 0 degrees.

For a viewer positioned perpendicular to one edge of a screen, a circle will appear less and less circular as the viewing angle from which it is perceived is enlarged. As the circle becomes increasingly elliptical, the ease with which it can be recognized as a circle diminishes. It turns out that the maximum acceptable viewing angle is 45 degrees. Beyond that the character or other image element risks becoming undecipherable.

Since it is quite typical to see alphanumeric text displayed in 80-character lines, we now understand that we must be sure that a viewer positioned perpendicular to the first character in the line be able reliably to read the 80th. And if the angle formed between that viewer's eye point and the 80th character must not exceed 45 degrees, then some simple trigonometry reveals everything we want to know about the front row.

Figure 2-7 illustrates a screen of width W. Lines drawn at 45 degrees from each edge of the screen intersect at a distance from the screen that is half of W. By definition, then, no one can sit closer to the screen than half its width and accurately read text at both of its edges.

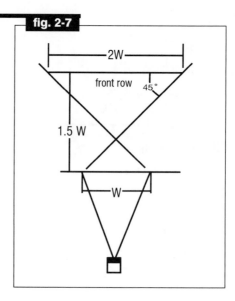

fig. 2-7

Beyond the 0.5W distance the lines diverge and form an ever-expanding cone that can, the further back we go, accommodate an ever-widening first row. Useful proportions to remember are that at a distance back from the display equal to 1.5 of its width, we can have a front row that is twice as wide as the screen (see Figure 2-7). At 2W back, the first row can be 3W. And so on.

3

PROJECTION

SCREENS

edited by **M.K. MILLIKEN**

Kim Milliken, of Da-Lite Screen
Company and founder of Optixx
Screen Systems, spent more
than 25 years in the audiovisual
industry. He is best known for
his commitment to educating
the industry with a level of
intelligence and sophistication
that remains unparalleled.

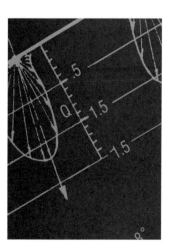

here was a time when the merits of front projection (FP) versus rear projection (RP) were thought to be relative and dependent on the application involved. For reasons that will be explained, that is no longer the case. Rear projection (RP) is to be considered optically preferable and superior in all cases.

The phase "optically preferable" was used to establish the increased presentation performance of rear projection in those scenarios where its strengths, primarily its image quality in ambient light, are useful or required. Other RP strengths include contrast enhancement means and the absence of potential projection beam shadows caused by errant audience attendees. However, rear projection has its limits, beyond which lie scenarios where only front projection is practical and where rear projection is not feasible. Cost of RP is always a factor. All else being equal, its price tag per square foot of projected area often is higher than its FP counterpart in a similar scenario. Impractical RP scenarios in AV applications include those where exceptionally large screen sizes are specified, where a back projection booth is too costly or architecturally prohibitive, in theater style scenarios, and even in smaller screen sizes where a contained cabinet enclosure isn't possible.

Principle of front projection screens

The principle of reflection is illustrated in Figure 3-1. If we imagine that a front screen is a mirror, then we could say that light rays leave the projector through its lens, travel in straight (but diverging) lines, and impinge upon the screen's surface, from which they are reflected into the audience area.

Front screen works by reflection

FIG. 3-1

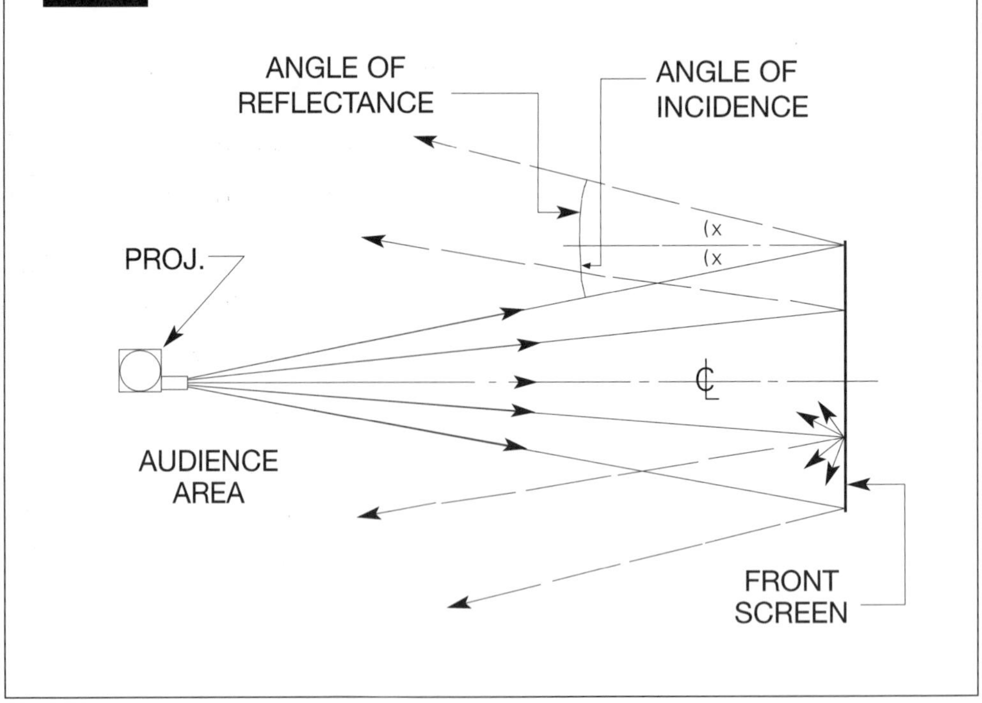

ANGLE OF REFLECTANCE

ANGLE OF INCIDENCE

PROJ.

AUDIENCE AREA

FRONT SCREEN

An actual mirrored surface would cause the reflected rays to return in an ever-widening pattern, inasmuch as their angles of incidence must equal their angles of reflectance when the reflection is specular. *Specular* is an optical term that means a surface behaves "like a polished mirror."

Real screens, of course, are not mirrors. If they were, viewers would see no image on the screen at all. Rather they would see only the bright light of the projection lamp shining into their eyes by reflection as if they stood in front of the screen looking back at the projector. Although not mirrors, many fronα screens are reflectors, but their reflection is diffuse, not specular. Nevertheless, the mirror concept is helpful for understanding how a front screen tends to work, depending on how specular – or diffuse – its surface is. The mix of specular and diffuse reflection components describes the light distribution characteristics of a particular FP screen.

Basic types of front projection screens

In most cases it is diffusion at the surface of an FP screen that makes it possible for an image projected upon it to be seen across a range of viewing angles in the audience. There are two prominent types of AV front projection screens. These two FP screen types differ in the means employed to achieve a mix of specular and diffuse reflection components. While there are a few variations to each of these types of FP screens, along with some lesser exceptions from antiquity (beaded screens for example), the same principles apply to them all.

The matte white screen, commonly constructed by incorporating white pigment particles into or onto the FP screen surface, produces only the diffusion component without specular, mirror-like action. The hybrid diffuser screen, commonly constructed by incorporating metallic particles onto the FP screen surface, produces a mixture of diffuse and specular reflection in a proportion determined by its design. This screen type is sometimes called a partial diffuser.

Matte white screens are essentially white paint. Having no specular component, they appear to the eye to be just white. And since they exhibit no mirror-like specular properties in their light distribution, matte white screens distribute the projector's light evenly in all directions, producing equal brightness to the eye at any viewer location.

By contrast, hybrid diffuser screens, composed of metallic paint or roughened metal plating, appear to the eye to be "silver" in color (although they actually are made of aluminum pigments or plating). Because the relative mixture of specular and diffuse components can be varied in the design of hybrid diffuser screens, various light distribution characteristics can be provided. Depending on the proportion of mirror-like properties to diffusion properties, these screens can be very directional and the image brightness very sensitive to viewer location.

Key FP screen properties

As full diffusers without a specular component, matte white screens exhibit only diffusion properties, while hybrid (partial) diffusers exhibit a mixture of specular and diffusion properties. The physical processes of diffusion and specularity involve different laws of physics. In the context of the two basic types of FP screens, specularity is the process of reflecting light governed by the law of reflection, while diffusion is the process of scattering light governed by Lambert's law (a.k.a. the law of scattering). For the most part, the physical properties of reflection and scattering are virtually opposite to each other. This might lead one to gather that the two types of screens behave in opposite ways, and that assumption would be correct.

As mentioned earlier in the discussion of specular mirrors, the law of reflection states that, relative to the surface perpendicular, the angle of incidence equals the angle of reflection. Therefore the location of the light distribution constituting the viewing zone produced by the FP hybrid diffuser screen, with its substantial mirror-like component, will depend upon where the projector is located (angle of incidence) and where the viewer is located (angle of reflection).

On the other hand, Lambert's law of diffuse scattering states that a purely diffuse surface will produce a light distribution such that equal brightness is measured in all directions off the perpendicular, regardless of the angle of incidence. Therefore the light distribution constituting the viewing zone produced by a matte white screen will be the same and independent of the location of projector and viewer.

Understanding these two opposite FP screen behaviors obviously is important in the design and setup of AV front projection scenarios. The two principles are quite easy to demonstrate. Crumple a piece of aluminum foil, then open it flat. With a table or ceiling lamp approximately behind you, hold the flattened foil at arm's length and move it in various directions, thereby simulating a range of angles of incidence and reflection off a hybrid diffuser between light source and you, the viewer. You will notice the reflected brightness visible on the roughened foil varies widely, depending on its angular attitude. Now repeat the process with a sheet of white paper, thereby simulating the matte white under similar conditions. You will notice the reflected brightness visible on the white paper is constant and does not change with its angular attitude.

Principle of rear projection screens

The principle of transmission is shown in Figure 3-2. If we imagine that a rear projection screen is a transparent sheet of glass or plastic, then we could say that light rays leave the projector through its lens, travel in straight (but diverging) lines, and impinge upon the screen's surface, through which they are transmitted into the audience area.

Rear screen works by transmission

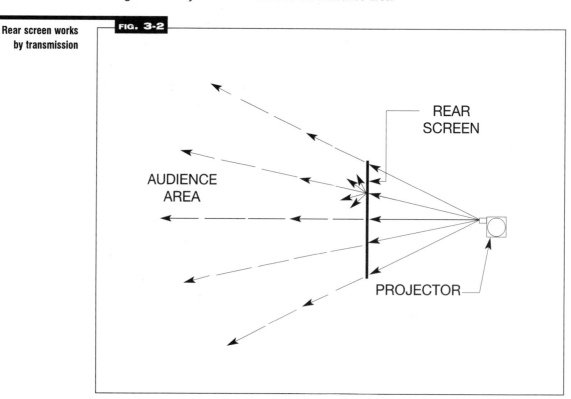

FIG. 3-2

REAR SCREEN

AUDIENCE AREA

PROJECTOR

A truly transparent screen, of course, would permit the rays to travel undeviated, with an ever-widening pattern similar to the one just described for reflective front screens.

However, just as front screens are never truly reflective, the rear screen is never truly transparent. If it were, again we would be looking right into the projection lamp, an effect similar to looking directly into an automobile headlight. But again, the transparent screen concept is useful for understanding how a rear screen tends to work, depending on the diffuseness of its surface. While the same principle encountered in front projection screens still applies in the case of rear projection screens, there are caveats in transmission optics which tend to complicate matters.

Ambient light

Ambient light refers to any light, other than the projection beam, that is visible within the projection environment. It usually is discussed in a negative context, in terms of how it degrades or washes out the viewed projected image on the screen. However, ambient light also has a positive context. Some degree of ambient light is not only appropriate, but also necessary to effective AV installations in commercial and business environments. Any presentation with a purpose other than entertainment requires an ambient light level sufficient for its participants to see the presenter, see each other, and see to take notes or read printed text. Only in certain entertainment venues (where the sole requirement of the audience is emotional involvement) is a zero level of ambient light appropriate.

Rear projection screens and ambient light

Rear projection screens perform well in lighted rooms because a portion of the ambient light incident to their surfaces is transmitted through the screen into the projection booth or cabinet enclosure, where it is safely absorbed by matte black, nonreflective surfaces lining the interior.

This ability not to reflect ambient light is the first of the two principle reasons that rear projection is always superior to projection in any environment where ambient light is a requisite.

The remaining portion of ambient light not transmitted through the screen into the booth or cabinet interior for absorption is still up for grabs. It may wash out the projected image to a degree, depending on the type of RP screen and its contrast enhancement means, if any.

Front projection screens and ambient light

Since front projection screens work essentially by reflected light, any ambient light incident to a front screen's surface will be returned by that screen in an identical way and added to the light from the projector. Thus any viewers positioned where some amount of the reflected ambient light reaches their eyes will experience degradation in the contrast of the projected image. In cases where the ambient light is strong enough, its effect on contrast can be so severe that the image becomes completely washed out.

The only way to depreciate this effect is to minimize as carefully as possible the amount of ambient light actually incident to the screen's surface. Even though there may be large areas of the audience chamber which are highly illuminated (desktops and so forth), as long as the ambient light falling on the screen is kept low, viewers should be able to experience at least adequate contrast within the projected images.

The shape of the viewing area

The viewing area is basically sector-shaped in both front and rear projection systems. Ideally its farthest boundary is formed by two 8H arcs that cross at the centerline of the screen and have their centers at the diagonally opposite sides of the screen, as diagrammed in Figure 3-3. The near boundary is formed by two lines displaced 60 degrees from the undeviated rays reflected from each side of the screen. It should be noted that each of these undeviated rays is the perfect reflection of a projection ray from the lens to the edge of the screen, where the angle of incidence is equal to the angle of reflectance. The limit of 45 degrees is imposed not to suggest that imagery viewed from larger angles would not be visible; it certainly would be. However, in contemporary high-resolution displays, visibility cannot be accepted as a minimum-viewing standard. Instead intelligibility must be the standard. As it is well understood that the human eye's ability accurately to identify characters and symbols from angles greater than 45 degrees is unreliable and precarious, a maximum bend angle of 45 degrees is generally considered prudent. The width of the front row is shown in Figure 3-3 as being twice as that of the screen, which, therefore, compels its distance back from the screen to equal $1\frac{1}{2}$ W.

**Front screen
seating area**

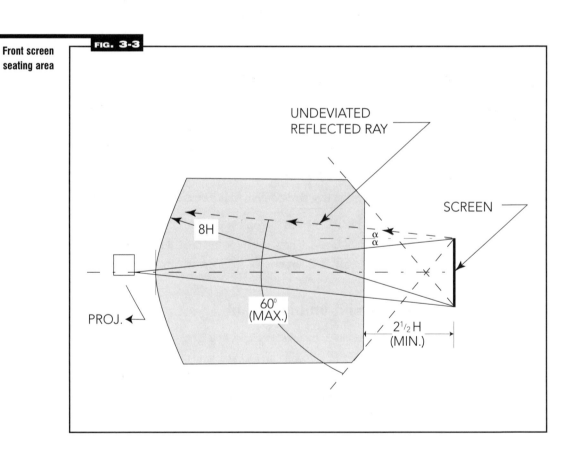

FIG. 3-3

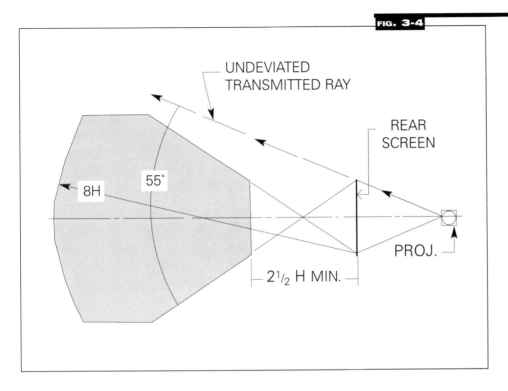

FIG. 3-4

**Rear screen
seating area**

The viewing area when side-by-side images are displayed

When dual images are projected, each image has its own viewing area, which is constrained by the identical geometry given in the preceding paragraphs. Figures 3-5 and 3-6 show that the viewing area for both screens combined, however, are reduced because the overlap of the two individual areas is partial.

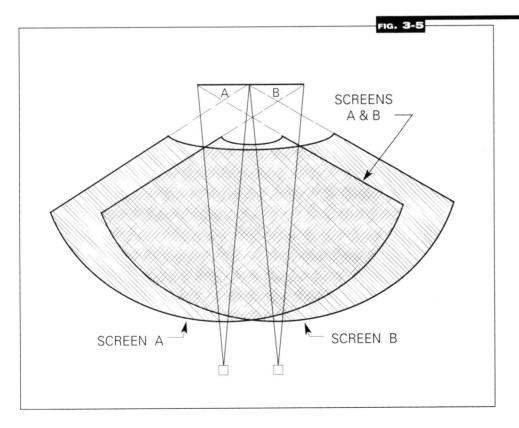

FIG. 3-5

**Dual images reduce
viewing area in front
projection system**

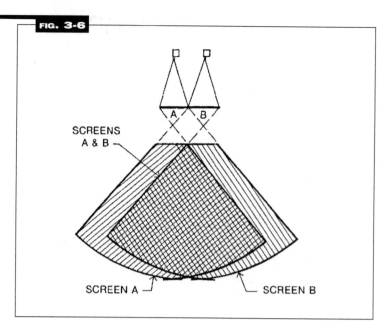

FIG. 3-6

SCREENS A & B

SCREEN A — SCREEN B

Projection screen performance

The projection screen is an important part of the AV projection display system that too often is taken for granted. The specification of a screen should be done with as much thought as selecting the projector itself. To describe the true function of the screen, projection display developers commonly use a car engine analogy. If we think of the projector as a car's engine, then the projection screen is analogous to the car's drive train. The engine provides the rotational power that moves the car down the road, but until the drive train transforms and distributes the engine's torque into linear motion, that power is not very useful. The situation is much the same in projection display. The projector provides the source of light power bundled directionally in a narrow beam, and the screen transforms it into a useful spatial volume that can be distributed to viewers. And, to continue the analogy, if we connect a Ferrari engine to a Chevy Nova drive train, we are likely to be disappointed in the overall performance. The same is true if we use a "luxury car" projector with a basic projection screen.

There are many kinds of projection screens, both front and rear. Each type has its own characteristics, which are chosen to satisfy a given application. Because rear projection is the most modern of AV screen products, the basic principles of projection screens are described first in terms of rear projection, but they also apply to front projection. Later in the chapter, both front and rear projection systems are examined.

The term *projection scenario* often is used in AV projection systems to describe the totality of factors brought together to satisfy the needs of a particular application. A scenario includes such properties as projection sense (front or rear), screen size, aspect ratio and location, throw distance, audience area and shape, ambient light conditions, projector type and viewer locations.

How a projection screen works

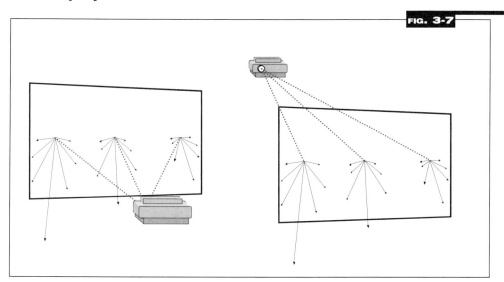

FIG. 3-7

Mini-screens behavior with respect to projected light rays

The function of any projection screen, front or rear, is to distribute the light incident to every area of its surface into every area of its audience. In the same way that a typical projected image is divisible into a matrix of its constituent pixels, we can imagine dividing a projection screen into a matrix of little "mini-screen areas." Figure 3-7 suggests how three of these randomly chosen "mini-screens" behave with respect to the projected light rays incident to them. The essential point to see here is that the key relationships between projector, screen and viewer are angular. Light rays that emanate from projectors are bundled into beams that diverge on their way to forming an image on the screen. Therefore, a light ray arriving at the edge of the screen always will have an incident angle significantly larger than the light ray aimed at the center of the screen.

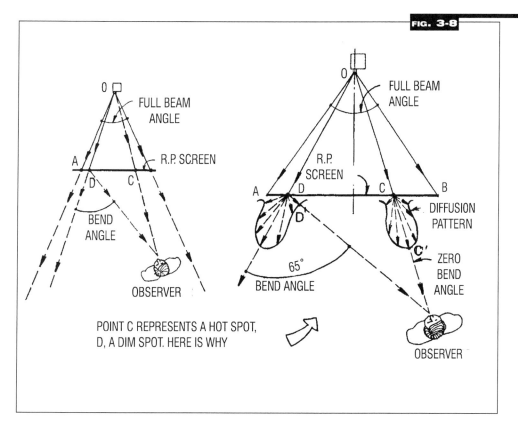

FIG. 3-8

Angular geometry

Figure 3-8 illustrates the varying angular geometry whereby each ray from the projector falls incident to the screen at a different angle depending on the ray's position at the screen. Keep in mind that in the top view shown in Figures 3-7 and 3-8 the rays appear relative to the screen's horizontal direction; this situation occurs only along the horizontal "meridian," that is, the imaginary horizontal line running from left to right through the center of the screen. If Figures 3-7 and 3-8 instead showed a side view of the geometry, the rays would appear relative to the vertical direction along the vertical meridian running top to bottom through the center of the screen. This seems a rather simple analysis in a two-dimensional drawing. In reality, projected rays travel through three-dimensional space, so that rays other than those along the two meridians—such as rays headed for the corners of the screen—follow compound angles that must be specified with both vertical and horizontal angular components.

Figure 3-8 also shows that the fundamental function of a projection screen is to distribute the light incident to every area of its surface into every area of its audience. While we have considered the projector's rays incident to various areas of the screen, we must also consider the rays from various areas of the screen to the observers.

Note in Figure 3-8 that the screen distributes light falling on the screen at points D and C across an angular range shown as "diffusion patterns" D' and C'. These patterns are merely polar plots of the light distribution function of a particular screen. (In a polar plot the length of the arrows depicts intensity at various angles.) For diffusion screens, these patterns vary somewhat depending on the light distribution characteristics of the particular screen, as well as the projection ray incident angle at any particular point on the screen.

Also depicted in Figure 3-8 is the "bend angle," or the angle between a particular point on the screen and the observer. As we know, the ray geometry formed by the projector and a point on the screen and between that point on the screen and the observer location is different for every point on the screen and every observer location. Notice in Figure 3-8 that at points D and C the observer location shown produces radically different bend angles through diffusion patterns D' and C'. The observer sees point C on the right side of the screen through the central rays of diffusion pattern C' (bend angle = 0 degrees), but sees point D on the left side of the screen through the extreme rays of diffusion pattern D' (bend angle = 65 degrees). The central ray of pattern C' is the longest in the polar plot, which means it depicts a view of the screen's distribution function that delivers to the observer its highest brightness. The extreme ray of pattern D' is the shortest in the polar plot, which means it depicts a view of the screen's distribution function that delivers to the observer its lowest brightness.

The hot spot

When all points on the screen are considered in this geometry, the observer will see a smoothly varying level of brightness in the screen image, from brightest to dimmest. This occurs because an observer's particular position is favored by the screen's light distribution function at points where the observer lines up with the projected rays (as at screen point C), and is disfavored by the light distribution function where the observer is substantially misaligned with the projected rays (as at screen point D). The result is that, for common diffusion screens, the observer will see a round "hot spot," shown at screen point C where the image appears brightest. The location of the hot spot on the screen image depends on the observer's location in the audience area. How visible or obvious the hot spot appears to the observer depends on the width of the diffuser's light distribution function.

FIG. 3-9

Diffusion at different angles
of incidence

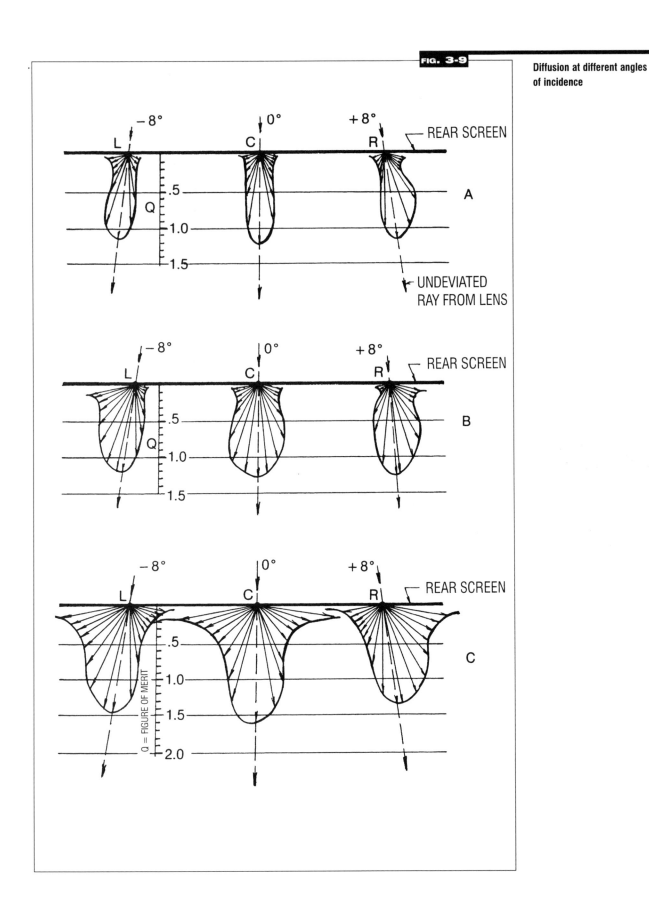

Figure 3-9 illustrates three different diffusion screens, A, B and C, with increasing amounts of diffusion. It shows how the diffusion pattern changes somewhat at three difference angles of incidence. Case A depicts narrow distribution of the projected light, case B depicts medium distribution of the projected light and case C depicts wide distribution of the projected light. Screen A, with the narrowest light distribution, will produce the most obvious (and objectionable) hot spot.

This effect of a particular screen's angular light distribution often is called "drop-off," because it refers to the drop in image brightness that occurs across the screen with increasing bend angle to the observer.

Screen brightness gain

Screen brightness gain is a relatively simple concept with some very complicated implications. All else being equal, a projection screen with a gain of 4 presents an image to the viewer that appears twice as bright as the image projected from a screen with a gain of 2. To measure screen gain, a photometer is pointed at the center of the screen at an angle of 0 degrees, and the reading is compared to one taken in an identical way when a matte white surface (ideally a block of $MgCO_3$) is substituted for the screen in question.

There is considerable irony in the fact that the term *brightness gain* is applied routinely to the projection screen and hardly ever to the projector. Yet it is the projector, not the projection surface, that is powered by electricity and comes with a gain dial marked "Brightness."

Irony aside, while both projector and screen are capable of increasing the brightness of the image, there is a substantive difference between attaining brightness through screen gain and attaining it through the projector's brightness control. Increasing the output of the projector is merely a matter of converting more electrons from the wall socket into more projected light (or more dollars from the user's wallet into a higher output projector). Neither of these "costs" directly affects other qualities of the projection system. However, attaining image brightness by increasing the brightness gain of the screen requires a sacrifice of a number of pertinent qualities of the system (described below). The most pertinent sacrifice is the angular width of the screen's light distribution. In other words, to achieve screen gain, its viewing area decreases.

From the discussion of bend angle and its relation to the screen's light distribution patterns in Figure 3-8, we know that the narrower the screen's angular light distribution and the narrower the audience viewing area, the quicker the brightness drop-off as the viewer moves to locations off center and the more pronounced or objectionable the hot spot. Viewing angle is precisely what we must trade away when we choose a higher gain screen over a lower gain screen. When screen gain increases, viewing angle must decrease.

The light distribution angles that determine the directions of the audience region into which the screen will send light, while shown on planar drawings as an area, actually occur in three-dimensional space and subtend a solid volume of space. Thus "solid angle" contains both vertical and horizontal angular dimensions, describing how densely the screen's light is distributed in space. The high-gain screen distributes its light into a small solid angle volume to produce high light density, while a low-gain screen distributes the same amount of light into a large solid angle, producing a low light density. Light density is perceived by the eye as brightness.

Why is the brightness of the screen measured only in the center? If a screen of gain 2.2 is more than two times brighter than matte white in the center, is it still brighter compared with the matte white at say, 45 degrees off axis? Not necessarily. A screen brightness gain relative to matte white occurs at all angles, giving rise to a "gain profile," which is the full function of how gain changes with angle. The single center point at 0 degrees is chosen only for simplicity and convention. Does this varying geometry between projected ray and viewer location mean that there is anything unique about the particular square foot of fabric of screen center? Of course not. No strip, area or square foot of screen material is manufactured to be different from any other. Optically, all areas of screen material are identical.

It is quite rare these days to see a projector vertically positioned exactly opposite to screen center. Much more frequently the projector is mounted parallel to the top or the bottom of the screen. When it is somewhere else, it still is not at 0 degrees but is instead perhaps 10 percent down (or up) from the screen's top (or bottom). Since it is unlikely for light reaching the center of the screen to be itself "on-axis," it is a little hard to see what could be the advantage of measuring light from an on-axis position.

The final observation to be made about gain is that the number we deduce from our measurements is not a number intrinsic to the screen itself, but one which is relative to a fixed, non-screen reference standard, generally a block of magnesium carbonate.

To all intents and purposes a flat expanse of $MgCO_3$ will absorb no light as it reflects and distributes all of the light incident to its surface (via Lambert's law or scattering) into a special pattern with perfect uniformity throughout all possible viewing angles. This point is subtle and deserves emphasis. Another way of expressing it is to say that light rays incident to a perfect matte white surface essentially will be fully scrambled such that all traces of their incident angles will be lost. Matte white projection screens get close to this theoretically perfect diffusion pattern, but only the $MgCO_3$ does it to perfection.

Thus the number displayed by a photometer aimed at an illuminated block of $MgCO_3$ will not vary as the instrument is moved through any number of random viewing angles. And, to make the experiment really interesting, our number also will remain invariant if we move our light source through an equally large and equally arbitrary range of projection angles.

There is, then, no combination of positions for the projection and measuring device which will yield a greater or lesser amount of brightness from this, the common reference standard against which we calculate screen gain. When we say "against" the standard we mean dividing the two numbers:

Screen Gain $= B_s / B_r$

where B_s is the brightness of the screen under test and B_r is the brightness of the matte white sample under exactly the same conditions. If the matte white is measured relative to itself such that $B_s = B_r$, then $B_r / B_r = 1$. Thus, pure matte white has a gain of 1.0.

What is confusing about all this is that from this equation it becomes obvious that the reference standard itself has gain = 1.0, when in fact gain is the very thing it doesn't have. A projection screen has gain when from one specific angle of view (0 degrees) it can be measured as being brighter than the reference standard. This is really what screen gain signifies—an increase by some amount over the unity (1.0) gain of $MgCO_3$.

Screen surfaces vary according to their gains

There is only one screen surface that has no gain and behaves identically to the reference standard. This is the ubiquitous and extraordinarily useful matte white projection screen. Array an audience before a matte white surface and you can be sure that all of its members, regardless of the projection angle or of their viewing angles, will be assured of a picture that is consistently and equally uniform throughout (keep the room lights as low as possible however).

If we could trace a bundle of projected light rays striking a piece of matte white screen, what we would see is that the rays will bounce off the surface in a pattern that forms a perfect hemisphere. The equator of this hemisphere is flush with the plane of the screen and no matter where on its circumference we choose to look, we will always see that it is filled with the same amount of light density.

Now let's ask what happens if we vary the intensity of the incoming bundle of light rays. We could do this by fiddling with the brightness control on our projector or by switching out the projector itself for one with greater or lesser lumen output. Would anything change about our hemisphere?

Yes, one (but only one) thing will change. The radius of the hemisphere will get bigger as we increase the amount of light filling it. So there is a directly proportional relationship between the volume of light (commonly called total luminous flux) available from the projector and the volume of the resultant hemisphere. Varying the flux, however, has no effect whatever on the shape of the hemisphere. If we are using a matte white screen, that always remains constant.

If the screen is not matte white, if it has been manufactured to have a gain of 2, for example, what happens to the luminous flux reaching its surface?

As a specular reflective component is added to the screen to increase gain, the base of the hemisphere contracts and, as the distance to its "north pole" expands, it starts to adopt the shape of an extending tear drop whose outer surface is still curved but whose diameter grows smaller and smaller as the screen is given higher and higher gain.

Furthermore, the axis of the tear drop (the line from its base that extends through its "north pole") points in a direction that is increasingly dependent on the incident angle of the light rays filling it and will therefore be less and less perpendicular to the surface of the screen. Despite these transformations, however, the volume of the ever-lengthening tear drop will always be the same as that of the original hemisphere.

Interestingly, the shape of the lobe of light leaving a rear projection screen is not hemispheric, even when the screen has a gain of 1. While the volume of the screen's transmitted light remains directly proportional to the amount of luminous flux from the projector, the two never are equal. This is so because all rear projection screens fail to transmit all of the light incident to their back surfaces. Quite a significant percentage of the flux in fact will be reflected by those back surfaces and some additional (but smaller) percentage will be absorbed by whatever medium is used for the rear projection screen's substrates (typically acrylic or glass).

The gain of a rear projection screen is increased by arranging for the diffusion layer (the scattering medium) to be less and less dense. This results in more and more of the projected light rays being permitted to pass through the screen with their incident angles undisturbed.

The essential behavior, then, of both rear and front projection screens is not created by any direct manipulation of their displayed "brightness." Screens cannot create energy. That's what projectors are for. Screens can (and do!) control the angular distribution of that energy and by that process alone they create what is called their gain.

Other types of front projection screens

Certainly the most prominent of alternative front screen configurations is the curved screen. Figure 3-10 illustrates how projected light rays falling on a curved screen surface are reflected in a somewhat radial pattern, converging at a point directly on-axis to the screen's center. A viewer positioned at this location will see the entire screen with uniform brightness, and other viewers nearby will enjoy a similarly good image. The "typical viewer" in the drawing, for example, when observing the three target areas of the screen, L, C, and R, has a bend angle from L and from R that is measurably less than if the screen were flat. (The angle from C, of course, is the same.)

A flat screen, unless it is matte white, tends to reflect its principal rays in a diverging pattern, therefore they do not converge at any specific viewing position. Consequently, if the gain of a curved screen is kept comparable to its flat screen alternative, the brightness uniformity from the curved screen will be better.

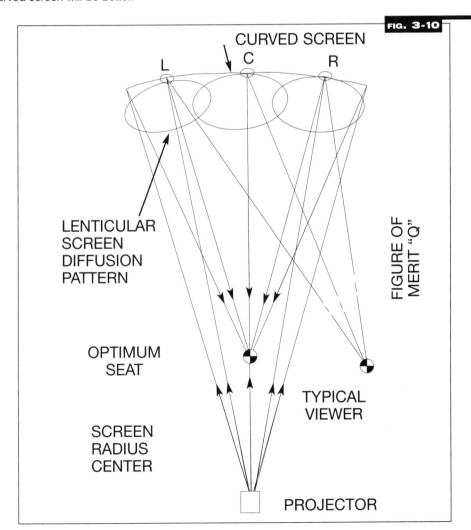

FIG. 3-10

Curved screen directs more light to audience area than flat screen of same material

CURVED SCREEN

L   C   R

LENTICULAR SCREEN DIFFUSION PATTERN

FIGURE OF MERIT "Q"

OPTIMUM SEAT

TYPICAL VIEWER

SCREEN RADIUS CENTER

PROJECTOR

Glass beaded screens

What is it about glass beads that makes them useful to a projection screen in the first place? The answer is that the screen behaves as though it were partially retro-reflective.

When a screen (or any other reflecting device) is made to be retro-reflective, the angle of reflection is not paired with an equal and opposite angle of incidence. The angle of incidence is the angle of reflection. In other words, when light rays strike a retro-reflective surface, most of them bounce back along their exact path of entry and therefore end up returned to the projection source from which they came.

Figure. 3-11 shows a series of brightness measurements (the Y-axis) made from just behind a projector (0 degrees on the X-axis) that was first positioned normally to a glass beaded screen (the solid line) compared with another series taken when the projector was moved 20 degrees off of the normal (the dashed line). Noticing the degree of the normal to which the two plots are unshifted and identical in slope, it is easy to see why glass beaded screens are assumed to be retro-reflective.

Brightness measurements on the Y and X axis

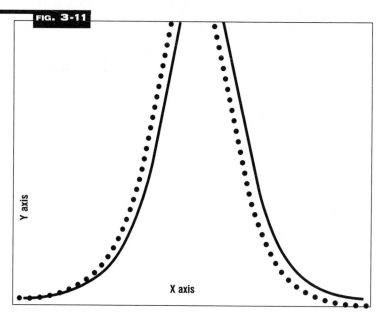

FIG. 3-11

To understand how glass beads really work, however, we first need to recall a little bit about an optical phenomenon called refraction. This is the process which governs the change in direction which light rays undergo when they cease traveling through one medium (air, for example) and start to travel through another with a different density (glass or plastic, for example).

If the medium the light is leaving is less dense than the medium it is entering, the refraction process will bend the light toward what is called the "normal" of the denser medium. When light exits a denser medium, it is bent away from that same "normal." The amount of bending (in either direction) is proportional to the difference in densities between the two media.

Figure 3-12 illustrates a bundle of projected light rays striking a single glass bead located somewhere out near the left-hand edge of a glass-beaded screen surface. Because glass is denser than air, each ray is refracted through a specific number of degrees toward the "normal"—which in the case of a sphere is a radius—a line connecting the point on the surface where the incoming light ray strikes and the center of the sphere. Notice that the spherical shape of the refracting surface causes all of the light rays in the bundle to converge such that they will reach the bottom of the sphere very much more tightly clustered than when they entered it.

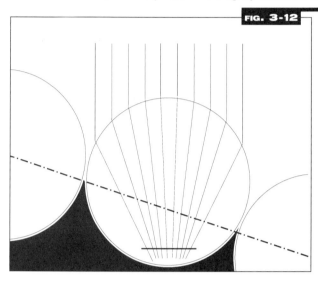

FIG. 3-12

Projected light rays striking the single glass bead

If, after passing through the back surface of the sphere, the light rays encountered air (a less dense medium) they would, of course, be refracted away from the normal (all those radii). But instead of air they strike a matte white diffuser, into which the sphere's underside has been tightly embedded. (For contrast purposes only this diffuser has been shaded black in Figures. 3-12 and 3-13).

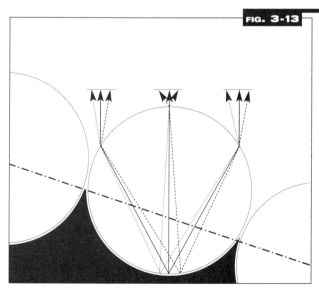

FIG. 3-13

Reflection off the back surface of a glass bead

Because it is a perfect diffuser, the matte white reflects all of the light back up through the sphere, which now can be thought of as a microscopic rear projection screen that images just that little area of illuminated diffusion beneath it. Note that when the reflected light rays reach the top of the sphere and reemerge into the air, they are refracted away from the normal (those radii again), which conveniently happens to mean that they are bent back toward the projector.

The Fresnel lenticular—another type of RP screen

While conventional front and rear projection screens spread the light in all directions, Fresnel lenticular screens enhance the image for optimum viewing by combining the focusing abilities of a Fresnel lens with the distributive properties of lenticular lenses. The result is up to four times greater brightness and extremely uniform images without "hot spots" and dark corners. Contrast is the key to the perfect image, especially when using single lens projectors, which often are very bright but have relatively poor black-levels, especially in brightly lit rooms and outdoor environments.

The Fresnel principle was developed by French physicist Augustin Jean Fresnel as a means of reducing the huge bulky lenses required for lighthouses. The basic principle is based on the fact that the curved and angled parts of the lens bend the light, and that by splitting the lens elements into sections a much smaller, lighter and cheaper lens could be made. By inducing this principle in the optical rear projection screen it is possible to control the light rays from the projector in such a way that all rays are directed to go perpendicularly out from the screen although entering the screen in different angles.

The Fresnel lens on an optical rear projection screen consists of thousands of concentric lens element rings, each having a different and specific angle or curvature to bend the light. Basically, the Fresnel lens ensures a perfect light distribution with an even luminance from the screen. In order to convert the light rays to an image, the optical screen also needs a diffusion layer.

The Fresnel lens on an optical rear projection screen

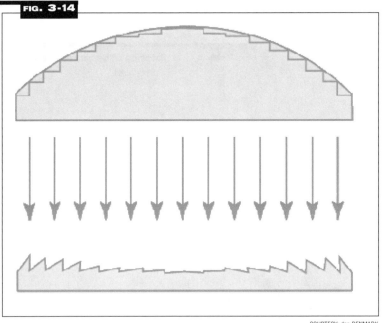

FIG. 3-14

COURTESY: dnp DENMARK

4

PROJECTION

OPTICS

edited by **M.K. MILLIKEN**

Kim Milliken, of Da-Lite Screen
Company and founder of Optixx
Screen Systems, spent more
than 25 years in the audiovisual
industry. He is best known for
his commitment to educating
the industry with a level of
intelligence and sophistication
that remains unparalleled.

This section covers information and facts about projection optics that are vital to the understanding of projection systems. Before turning to some of the optical theories that have to do with projection system design, let's look at lenses.

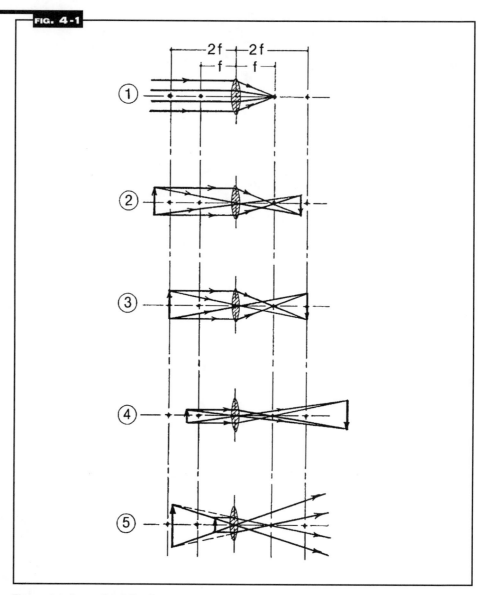

FIG. 4-1

Figure 4-1 shows the following:

Case 1. When the object is located an infinite distance from the lens, the merging light rays are parallel. They are brought to a focus at the focal point located on the opposite side of the lens. Obviously the lens works the same in either direction.

Case 2. When the object is located anywhere between 2f (focal length) and infinity, the image is formed on the opposite side of the lens between f and 2f. The image is inverted, smaller and real, which means that it can be seen on a screen placed at its location in space.

Case 3. When the object is located exactly at 2f, the image is formed on the opposite side of the lens at 2f. It is inverted, the same size and real.

Case 4. When the object is located between f and 2f, the image is formed beyond 2f on the opposite side of the lens and is inverted, magnified and real.

Case 5. When the object is located at a distance less than f, the image appears on the same side of the lens as the object and, hence, cannot be projected. Note also that in this case the image is erect, not inverted. Such an image is called virtual (and, thus, not "real") and can be seen directly by the eye. This is the principle of the common magnifying glass.

If the object were to be placed exactly at f, the reverse of Case 1 (in Figure 4-1) would occur; the outgoing rays would be parallel and no image could be formed. If we now consider that the object is a plane of illuminated pixels or a film frame, and the image is at a projection screen location, then Case 4 in Figure 4-1 represents the normal projection situation wherein a small object is projected magnified on a projection screen.

The "thin lens" concept shown in Figure 4-2 is useful in performing certain calculations dealing with object/image relationships in projection optics. It assumes there is a single, thin, convex lens with its optical plane symmetrically placed at the center of its thickness. Object and image distances S'and S are measured from this plane, and their sum equals the distance from the projector aperture to the screen.

FIG. 4-2   Thin lens geometry

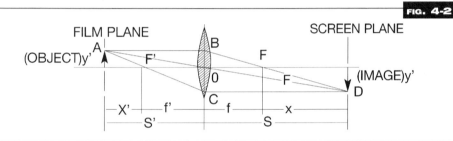

1. Δ ABC - ΔF'OC

2. $\therefore \dfrac{BC}{S'} = \dfrac{OC}{f'}$ OR $\dfrac{y' + y}{S'} = \dfrac{y}{f'}$

3. LIKEWISE, IN Δ BCD & Δ BOF
$\dfrac{BC}{S} = \dfrac{BO}{f}$ OR $\dfrac{y' + y}{S'} = \dfrac{y'}{f}$

4. ADDING 2 AND 3:
$\dfrac{y' + y}{S'} + \dfrac{y' + y}{S} = \dfrac{y}{f'} + \dfrac{y'}{f}$

5. BUT $f = f'$

6. $\therefore \dfrac{y' + y}{S'} + \dfrac{y' + y}{S} = \dfrac{y' + y}{f}$

7. FROM WHICH
$\dfrac{1}{S'} + \dfrac{1}{S} = \dfrac{1}{f}$ THIS IS THE "LENS FORMULA"

8. SOLVING FOR
$\dfrac{1}{S'} = \dfrac{1}{f} - \dfrac{1}{S'}$:

9. MULTIPLYING THROUGH
BY S: $\dfrac{S}{S'} = \dfrac{S}{f} - \dfrac{S}{S} = \dfrac{S}{f} - 1$

10. NOW USING SIMILAR TRIANGLES AOB & COD:
$\dfrac{y}{y'} = \dfrac{S}{S'} = M$
WHERE M IS THE MAGNIFICATION

11. NOW SUBSTITUTING M FOR $\dfrac{S}{S'}$ IN STEP 9:
$M = \dfrac{S}{f} - 1$ OR $\dfrac{S}{f} = M + 1$

12. AND SOLVING FOR S:
$S = f(M + 1)$
WHERE S IS THE DISTANCE FROM THE CENTER OF A THIN LENS TO THE SCREEN.

13. IN A SIMILAR MANNER, BY MULTIPLYING 9. BY S' INSTEAD OF S ETC., WE CAN SHOW THAT:
$S' = f\left(\dfrac{1}{M} + 1\right)$
WHERE S' IS THE DISTANCE FROM THE CENTER OF A THIN LENS TO THE APERTURE.

We shall see shortly that when we make use of the more practical "compound lens" formulas, the object and image distances are measured from the front and rear (glass) surfaces of the lens. Because the simple lens equation ignores the existence of the nodes of admission and emission in a compound lens, an error in the distance from aperture to screen can be introduced.

While the compound lens equations take this nodal distance into account, this also can be done automatically by summing the back focus (BF), front focus (FF) and glass-to-glass length (L) of the lens assembly to yield the correct distance between the front and rear focal points of the given lens.

Equations for object/image relationship using a simple thin lens

Let us examine the geometry of the simple lens shown in Figure 4-2.

Note how the rays are formed for the case of the simple lens. Ray A-B is drawn parallel to the optical centerline so that it will emerge from the lens and pass through the front focal point. This follows from Case 1 in Figure 4-1, which shows that any ray emanating from, or passing though, the focal point will emerge on the other side of the lens parallel to the optical axis.

Ray A-F'-C is drawn through the back focal point F' so that it also will emerge parallel to the optical axis shown in Figure 4-2. The two rays A-B-F-D and A-F'-C-D intersect at point D, where they form the image of arrowhead A.

A third ray, A-O-D, drawn through the center of the lens, O, also serves to locate point D. In Figure 4-1, the lens was conveniently drawn large enough to intersect all three rays, but even if it were not that large the same geometric construction can be drawn simply by extending the vertical center line B-C such that it intersects the rays A-B and A-F'-C. This situation is illustrated in Figure 4-3.

Method of ray tracing when rays fall outside of lens

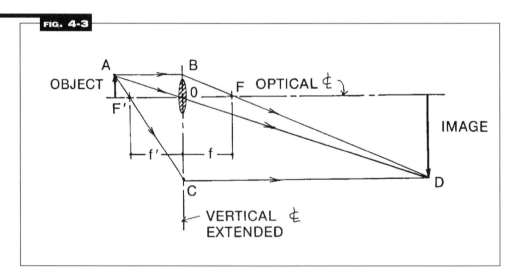

FIG. 4-3

In Figure 4-2, Equation 9 is called the "lens formula." It is used in elementary lens problems to solve for any one of its three variables when the other two are known. Although Equations 11 and 13 also often appear in articles on projection optics, equations describing the behavior of compound lenses are more practical for AV design calculations.

Equations for object/image relationship using a compound lens

Equations 5, 7, 8 and 9 in Figure 4-4 are useful S' formulas because they take into account that projection lenses contain several elements and have, therefore, appreciable lens barrel length. The basic dimensions x and x' are measured from the front and rear focal points respectively. The actual throw distance S and its conjugate S' are measured from the front and rear surfaces of the lens. We do not, therefore, have to know anything about what goes on optically within the lens.

FIG. 4-4

Compound lens geometry

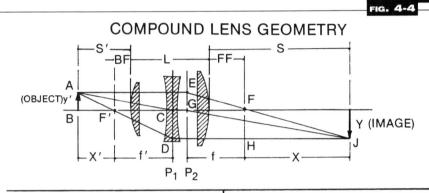

COMPOUND LENS GEOMETRY

1. $\triangle ABF' \sim \triangle F'CD$

2. $\therefore \frac{AB}{X'} = \frac{CD}{f'}$, OR

3. $\frac{y'}{x'} = \frac{y}{f}$ (BECASE $f' = f$)

4. LIKEWISE, IN $\triangle EGF$ & $\triangle FHJ$
   $$\frac{FH}{x} = \frac{EG}{f}, \text{ OR}$$

5. $\frac{y}{x} = \frac{y'}{f}$

6. FROM 3:
   $$\frac{y}{y'} = \frac{f}{x'}$$

7. BUT $\frac{y}{y'} = M =$ MAGNIFICATION

8. $\therefore M = \frac{f}{x}$, FROM WHICH

9. $x' = f(\frac{1}{M})$ WHERE $x' =$ DISTANCE FROM F'

10. TO FILM PLANE.
    FROM 5: $\frac{y}{y'} = \frac{x}{y} = M = $ MAGNIFI- CATION

11. FROM WHICH $x = f(M)$ WHERE $x =$ DISTANCE FROM F TO SCREEN. IT IS NOW OBVIOUS THAT THE THROW DISTANCE IS THE SUM OF FRONT FOCUS FF AND DISTANCE x, OR:

12. $S = x + FF$ THIS IS THE ONLY PRACTICAL WAY TO COMPUTE THROW DISTANCE.

13. LIKEWISE, $s' = x' + BF$

Reconciling equations for simple and compound lens analysis

A common definition for the "throw distance" of a projection lens is

$$TD = f(M + 1)$$

where

f = focal length

M = magnification which in turn is image height H divided by aperture height h or, alternatively, is image width W divided by aperture width w.

This is Equation 11 for simple lens analysis in Figure 4-2. Likewise, Equation 7 in Figure 4-4 for compound lens analysis often is given for throw distance. Thus

$$TD = f(M)$$

where f and M are the same as in the preceding equation.

Even though the two equations are by no means identical, they will yield the same throw distance when TD is measured from the same point.

Let us take the case of unity magnification, M = 1, and calculate the throw distance for both a simple and a compound lens, each with a 5" focal length. See A and B in Figure 4-5.

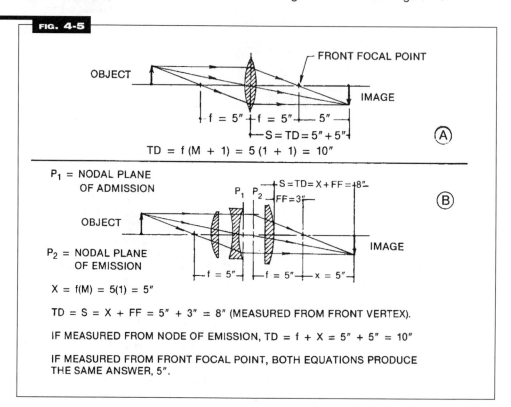

FIG. 4-5

OBJECT

FRONT FOCAL POINT

IMAGE

$f = 5"$ $f = 5"$ $5"$

$S = TD = 5" + 5"$

$TD = f (M + 1) = 5 (1 + 1) = 10"$

(A)

P_1 = NODAL PLANE OF ADMISSION

P_1 P_2

$S = TD = X + FF = 8"$

$FF = 3"$

(B)

OBJECT

IMAGE

P_2 = NODAL PLANE OF EMISSION

$f = 5"$ $f = 5"$ $x = 5"$

$X = f(M) = 5(1) = 5"$

$TD = S = X + FF = 5" + 3" = 8"$ (MEASURED FROM FRONT VERTEX).

IF MEASURED FROM NODE OF EMISSION, $TD = f + X = 5" + 5" = 10"$

IF MEASURED FROM FRONT FOCAL POINT, BOTH EQUATIONS PRODUCE THE SAME ANSWER, 5".

It is clear that if we attempted to measure the throw distance of 10" as found in Figure 4-5 for a thin lens (A), when actually we were confronting a compound lens, we would have difficulty. The optical center of a compound lens is not indicated on its barrel and it is very seldom located at the physical center of that barrel's length.

It is much more practical to measure from some point that is known, such as the front vertex of the lens. The front vertex is the center of the frontmost piece of glass (or plastic) in the lens assembly. We see that the 10" throw distance given by the simple lens formula is not practical because we do not use a thin lens in a projector and we do not have a reliable place from which to measure the 10" when using a compound lens. What is a practical distance, however, is the 8" distance we can measure from the front element of the compound lens to the screen.

Note that, for complete accuracy, the front focus distance (FF) must be added to the x = f(M) distance to arrive at the exact throw distance for a compound lens. For typical projection lenses, FF can be taken as 2/3 the focal length. Precise figures for FF, lens length L and back focus BF should be available from any lens manufacturer.

In Example 1, Figure 4-6, we see that, for a compound lens, an accurate distance from the plane of the slide or film to the screen is given by the sum of:

$x' = f\left(\dfrac{1}{M}\right) = \left(\dfrac{h}{H}\right)$ (all units in inches) This is equation 5, compound lens see (Figure 4-4.)

plus BF = back focus distance

plus L = length of compound lens, vertex to vertex, inches

plus FF = front focus distance, inches.

plus $x = f(M) = \left(\dfrac{h}{H}\right)f$ (all units in inches) This is equation 7, compound lens.

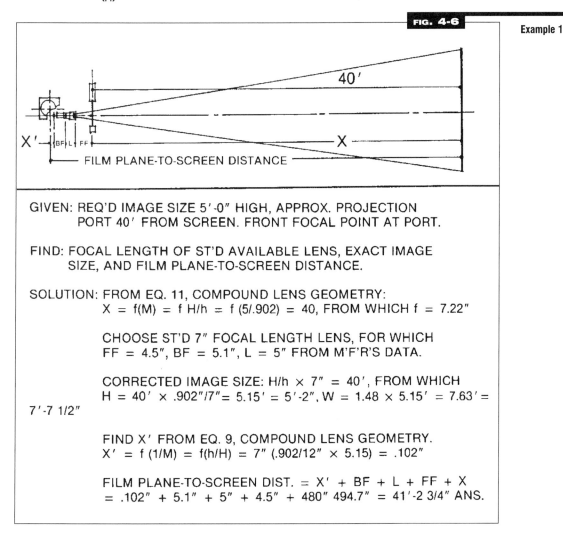

FIG. 4-6

Example 1

GIVEN: REQ'D IMAGE SIZE 5'-0" HIGH, APPROX. PROJECTION
PORT 40' FROM SCREEN. FRONT FOCAL POINT AT PORT.

FIND: FOCAL LENGTH OF ST'D AVAILABLE LENS, EXACT IMAGE
SIZE, AND FILM PLANE-TO-SCREEN DISTANCE.

SOLUTION: FROM EQ. 11, COMPOUND LENS GEOMETRY:
X = f(M) = f H/h = f (5/.902) = 40, FROM WHICH f = 7.22"

CHOOSE ST'D 7" FOCAL LENGTH LENS, FOR WHICH
FF = 4.5", BF = 5.1", L = 5" FROM M'F'R'S DATA.

CORRECTED IMAGE SIZE: H/h × 7" = 40', FROM WHICH
H = 40' × .902"/7"= 5.15' = 5'-2", W = 1.48 × 5.15' = 7.63' =
7'-7 1/2"

FIND X' FROM EQ. 9, COMPOUND LENS GEOMETRY.
X' = f (1/M) = f(h/H) = 7" (.902/12" × 5.15) = .102"

FILM PLANE-TO-SCREEN DIST. = X' + BF + L + FF + X
= .102" + 5.1" + 5" + 4.5" + 480" 494.7" = 41'-2 3/4" ANS.

We can see from Example 2, shown in Figure 4-7, that if we are calculating the distance from the slide or film aperture to the screen, both equations will give the same answer, with any slight difference due only to the distance between the two nodes. The lens exhibits the same focal length whether rays from a distant object enter the rear or front element of the lens.

Example 2

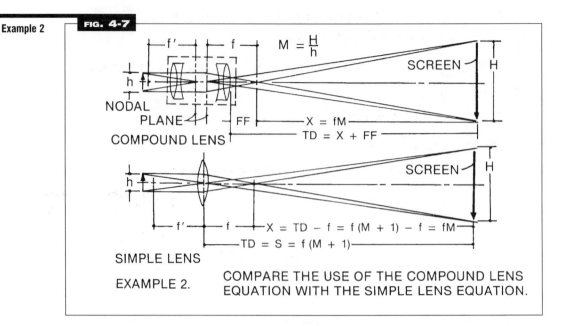

SIMPLE LENS

EXAMPLE 2. COMPARE THE USE OF THE COMPOUND LENS
EQUATION WITH THE SIMPLE LENS EQUATION.

But if we are calculating throw distance only, (x + FF) will be less than f(M+l) by an amount equal to (f-FF).

Again, because we do not use a simple lens in practice, the compound lens formula x = f(M) should be employed, with the FF distance added to obtain the throw distance from the front vertex of the lens to the screen.

Focal length and the effective focal length of a lens

In reality, there is no difference between these lengths. Nevertheless, because the terms are not always used interchangeably, a brief discussion is merited. The focal length of a lens is the distance from its node of emission to the image of a distant object formed by it. A familiar example of this is when we take rays from the sun (a distant object indeed) and focus them with a lens so that they converge onto a spot to ignite flammable material. If we turn this lens around so that its back element faces the sun, we can produce exactly the same hot spot. Thus a lens has the same focal length whether it is used backwards or forwards.

Lens focal length is the same, whether rays from a distant object enter the rear or front element of the lens

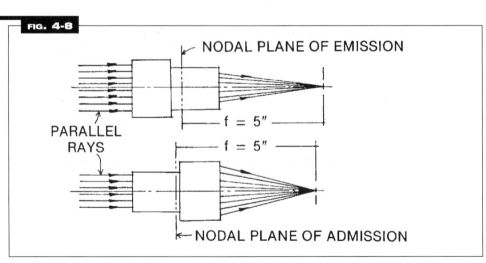

If we have a projection lens whose barrel is engraved 5" f : 3.5, we know that the focal length is 5" and the aperture stop is fixed as 3.5. We can aim this lens at the sun or at any object at least 600 feet away, focus the image on a white sheet of paper and measure the 5" focal length from the surface of the paper to a plane location on the outside of the lens barrel. This plane will mark the node of emission for the lens. Now, if we rotate the lens end for end, as diagrammed in Figure 4-8, aim the back end at the object and repeat the procedure, we will locate the node of admission.

The two nodal planes thus located may be ¹/₄" or more apart or they may overlap each other. Whatever the case, the distance between them is (unsurprisingly) known as the internodal distance. The significance of the two nodes is that they are the apparent planes from which the light rays seem to emanate when the lens is forming an image of a given object. The magnification between the nodal planes is always 1:1. It is possible, therefore, to draw geometric object and image rays without actually knowing how each element within the lens refracts.

Figure 4-9 shows nodal planes and ray paths for a simple object and image. With a simple thin lens, the nodes of admission and emission coincide at the center of the lens thickness. Everything else remains the same. The term *effective focal length* (EFL) came about because each element in a compound lens has its own focal length but, when they are combined into a compound lens assemblage, they exhibit only one focal length. Although it was natural to think of this as an "effective" focal length, that adjective is superfluous and the correct terminology is simply "focal length."

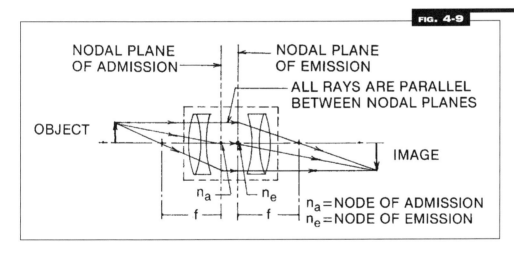

FIG. 4-9

Nodal planes and ray paths for a simple object and image

5

MIRRORS IN

PROJECTION

SYSTEMS

edited by **M.K. MILLIKEN**

Kim Milliken, of Da-Lite Screen
Company and founder of Optixx
Screen Systems, spent more
than 25 years in the audiovisual
industry. He is best known for
his commitment to educating
the industry with a level of
intelligence and sophistication
that remains unparalleled.

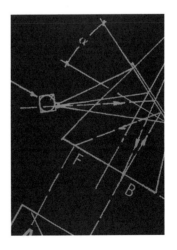

Mirrors are used in display systems principally to minimize the required depth of rear projection booths. With one or two mirrors correctly positioned behind a rear projection screen, the depth of a booth can be reduced by more than 50 percent.

This is reasonable because light rays coming out of a projector (any projector) must pass through a lens, which causes them to diverge. If they didn't do that and a projector were shined at a blank wall, the size of the image it cast could never be made bigger, no matter how far back from that wall it might be moved. To state that last sentence in a different way, to cast any image size there is a minimum distance back from the image at which a projector must be placed. This is called the throw distance.

Even though a particular system's throw distance cannot be reduced and although the light rays making up its image have to travel that distance if they are to form a picture big enough to fill its screen, they don't have to do it in unbroken straight lines. Their paths can be intersected with mirrors and, so long as the mirrors are at the correct angles, no distortion of any kind will occur. Alert readers will observe immediately that a mirror reverses an image, but compared with a front projection screen so will a rear screen. Fortunately this is a non-issue, as any video projector is certain to have a control that, when activated, will electronically "reverse" its image whichever way it appears. As long as the total path length of every light ray emanating from the projector is not changed by the insertion of a mirror or mirrors, the resultant image need not be degraded to any degree.

Ghosting

There are, however, two "artifacts" that can intrude upon an image's quality. One is called ghosting and the other is called a secondary reflection. The first thing to say about them is that they are not the same.

Calculating the angle of the mirror in rear projection

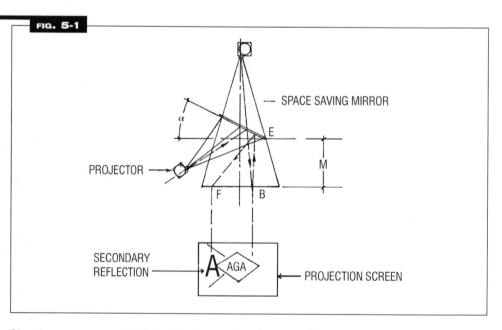

FIG. 5-1

Ghosting appears as a faint, double image wherein every object within the picture appears to be outlined by a slightly offset copy of itself. Instead of appearing sharply defined as in "clear," it looks "fuzzy." Ghosting is caused when there are, in fact, two image planes, one typically being the front surface of the rear screen and the other being its back surface.

In the case of a standard, acrylic rear projection screen, the two surfaces are separated by the thickness of the plastic sheet out of which it was made and, thus, are not more than a half-inch apart. That fractional inch, however, is quite enough to create a doubled image if the undiffused surface has had something done to it that has made it other than transparent. It is good practice on the part of the AV designer to ensure that the coated side of any diffusion screen is installed facing the audience and that nothing be done to the back surface, including allowing it to become dusty.

Technically there is another way to encounter ghosting. It entails using "second surface" mirrors. The reflective coatings of these mirrors are placed upon the surface behind the viewing surface. These mirrors are perfectly suitable for bathrooms (where their reflective coating cannot be scratched), but they are entirely inappropriate for projection display systems.

The reflective coating of "first surface" mirrors, by comparison, is applied to their front surfaces. It can be made out of rigid glass or Mylar® film. The latter obviously is much lighter in weight, while the former is more rigid and, thus, can be flatter.

Unfortunately both types of first surface mirrors can exhibit defects resulting from manufacturing errors; if present, these defects will be unacceptably visible in the displayed image. If a defective mirror has a film substrate, the artifact commonly will appear as a succession of diagonally parallel "zebra stripes" which will not be visible on the mirror surface but will, nevertheless, be distinctly apparent within the projected image.

If the defective mirror has a glass substrate, a different series of stripes will be visible which typically run parallel to the mirror's vertical or horizontal edges. These are called "draw lines." They result from imperfect manufacture of the glass substrate, which leaves it with tiny variations in surface flatness that are "copied" through the reflecting material deposited over them.

Secondary reflection

Secondary reflection is a problem that even non-defective mirrors can cause. This phenomenon is exhibited most often as faint repetitions of parts of the picture properly projected above the screen's equator; they show up as visible artifacts below the equator. What causes this is as easy to define as it has been difficult to avoid.

Earlier in this discussion we stressed that the back surfaces of diffusion screens must be kept clean and uncoated. Doing so means, consequently, that this clear surface definitely will be reflective. Some amount of light from the projector, therefore, will be reflected back toward the mirror on its first pass through the screen. Because mirror systems generally position the projector below the screen, the mirror closest to the screen will have its bottom edge farther away from the screen than its top; thus, looked at in elevation, its vertical plane will form some angle with the plane of the screen.

On reaching the top of the screen, some of the light rays from the projector will bounce back and hit the mirror for the second time, after which they will be reflected at angles different from the ones they traveled in their first bounce. If those second paths are along angles that are too small, the secondary light rays will pass not below the screen but visibly through it.

The challenge of figuring out correct geometries for mirror systems and projector angles behind a rear screen has bedeviled designers for years. However, secondary reflections can be avoided as follows.

The drawing in Figure 5-2 (first created by Raymond Wadsworth in 1983, which explains why the projector icon is a slide projector and why the drawing is not in elevation but in plan) shows the various distances that need to be manipulated in order to calculate α, the angle at which the mirror must be set so that secondary reflections will not occur. In contemporary mirror systems, this drawing should be rotated 90 degrees and "W/2" should be named "W2," as "W" stands here for width and we want "H' for height.

FIG. 5-2

HOW TO FIND FB IN TERMS OF W,M, AND T, WHERE B IS THE CRITICAL POINT THAT COULD REFLECT A RAY TO THE MIRROR AT POINT E, AND THEN TO THE SCREEN ALONG EF. α IS THE LIMITING MIRROR ANGLE. IF α IS REDUCED, POINT F WILL FALL ON THE SCREEN.

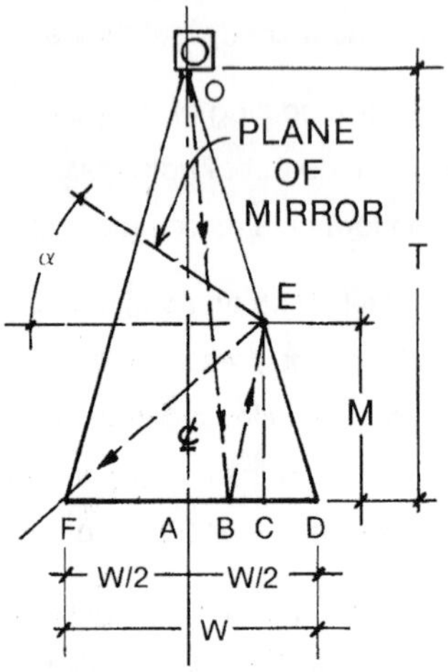

STEP 1. DRAW LIGHT BEAM TO SCALE. LOCATE DESIRED MIRROR POSITION E. DRAW EC⊥TO SCREEN.

STEP 2. FIND CD.
$\triangle$ CDE $\sim \triangle$ADO
$\therefore \dfrac{CD}{\frac{W}{2}} = \dfrac{M}{T}$ AND CD $= \dfrac{WM}{2T}$

STEP 3. FIND BC.
$\triangle$OAB $\sim \triangle$ EBC
$\therefore \dfrac{BC}{AB} = \dfrac{M}{T}$ AND BC $= \dfrac{(M)AB}{T}$

STEP 4. FIND AB IN TERMS OF BC, CD, & W/2
AB + BC $= \dfrac{W}{2} -$ CD. NOW SUBSTITUTE 2 & 3 IN 4:
$$AB = \dfrac{W(T-M)}{2(T+M)}$$

STEP 5. FIND FB: FB = FA + AB $= \dfrac{W}{2} + \dfrac{W}{2}\left(\dfrac{T-M}{T+M}\right)$

OR FB $= \dfrac{W}{2}\left[1 + \dfrac{T-M}{T+M}\right]$

PLANE OF MIRROR

All the angular relationships that are detailed, however, are as useful today as they were years ago. To find the minimum value for α, the equations require three data points:

1) the height (for Wadsworth it was the width) of the screen;

2) the throw distance;

3) the distance back from the screen to the closest edge of the mirror (in the drawing this is a side edge; in our case it is the top edge).

Plugging those three numbers into the formula yields, for any mirror system, the minimum angle at which the mirror must be set so that all of the light rays reflected back by the screen strike the mirror in such a way that, when they are reflected by it a second time, they travel along paths leading either above or below the screen but never through it.

6

M E A S U R I N G

L I G H T

edited by **M . K .   M I L L I K E N**

Kim Milliken, of Da-Lite Screen
Company and founder of Optixx
Screen Systems, spent more than
25 years in the audiovisual
industry. He is best known for his
commitment to educating the
industry with a level of
intelligence and sophistication
that remains unparalleled.

When people first set out to quantify visible light, they chose as their standard a source that was familiar and common to all: a candle. Yes, it had to be a specifically sized candle, made of a specific material and molded in a specific way, but it was an ordinary candle nonetheless. The amount of light emitted from such a candle became our first and most fundamental unit of brightness. It is called 1 candlepower.

Candlepower

If such a candle is lighted at the center of an otherwise darkened room, we can see from walking around it that its energy is radiating equally in all directions. It also is apparent that the farther we retreat from its flame the less light it appears to be shedding. Although those two facts are straightforward enough, some powerful deductions can be made from them. Generalizing from the observations, we can state that light from a point source (the candle) radiates outward in all directions such that it uniformly illuminates the surface of an ever-expanding sphere. As the radius of that sphere gets larger and larger, the surface area grows at an even faster rate and thus the energy from the candle is spread ever more thinly.

Since the surface area of a sphere of radius r is given by $4\pi r^2$, we can see that a radius of 1 foot will give us a surface area of 12.56ft^2 (or 4πft^2, since r^2 = 1). Increase the radius to 2 feet, however, and the surface area jumps to 50.27 ft^2. When r = 3 feet, the surface area balloons to 113.10 ft^2. This is the inverse square law. Mathematically it states that the illumination from a light source varies inversely to the square of its distance from the measuring point. This, among many other things, explains why a 6 x 8' screen (48 ft^2) isn't half as bright as a 3 x 4' display (12 ft^2); it is a fourth as bright, even though the throw distance (r) has merely doubled.

Now suppose that in addition to defining a unit of emitted light (the candlepower) we wish to establish some standard for measuring light incident to a surface area. Let's place our candle at the center of a sphere with a convenient radius of 1'. Now let's calculate the amount of our candle's energy that is incident to just one square foot of the sphere's surface. And, because it makes perfect sense, let's call that quantity 1 footcandle.

The next step we want to take concerns deciding exactly what fraction of the energy in 1 candlepower is expended in the production of 1 footcandle. We need this new unit because when we come to consider light sources other than candles we recognize that some of them, video projectors, for example, do not radiate spherically but beam all their output in just one specific direction. They illuminate, therefore, only a section of the sphere surrounding them and we want some way of accounting for that.

Lumens

As the radius of the sphere is still 1, the total surface area is 12.56 ft^2 (4π again). Since we are interested only in one of those square feet, it follows that our new unit will equal 1 candlepower divided by 12.56. Let us call this unit 1 lumen.

Understanding the relationship between a footcandle and a lumen enables us to calculate precisely how much light will fall on a screen of any specified size from a projector of some specified lumen output. All we need to know is the requisite throw distance (the r of our formula). Given the footcandles, we are equally adept at solving backwards to determine the lumens.

Now we know how to express numerically the brightness of a light source. We also know how to quantify the light emanating from that source as it illuminates a distant surface. What happens if that surface is a projection screen, which is reflective (or transmissive)? How will we quantify the brightness it may reradiate?

To answer those questions, let's stick with the square foot concept and make our newest unit a measure of the light coming off 1 ft^2 of surface. What energy unit would be appropriate to choose? Let's use the lumen again and declare that 1 square foot of surface radiating 1 lumen of light is producing 1 foot Lambert.

To tie all this together neatly we need just a few more terms, the first of which is the word *flux*. Technical people like to say flux when they are referring to a flow of energy. (When they quantify such a flow onto a surface, incidentally, they will say flux density.)

Another term popular with scientific people is *solid angle*. An ordinary angle of the kind we draw on a piece of paper has just two dimensions (and often is called a plane angle). The angle formed at the vertex of the cone of a projection beam, however, has three dimensions and therefore is deemed to be solid. (Thought about in this light, we can generalize that a solid angle must always be formed by at least three intersecting planes, the intersection of two walls and a ceiling being a typical example.)

With this small vocabulary in mind, we should be ready to decipher a full-blown, scientific definition:

> A lumen is equal to the luminous flux through a unit solid angle from a uniform point source of one candle, or to the flux on a unit surface area all points of which are at a unit distance from a uniform point source of one candle.

We can also state that an intensity of 1 lumen/ft^2 equals 1 footcandle.

And we will concisely define the foot Lambert as a unit of luminance equal to 1 lumen/ft^2.

Using the metric system

Can we convert our definitions to the metric system? Of course. Notice that our expanded lumen definition has already freed us from reliance on any particular distance unit. Any consistent unit will serve.

Let's start with the same candle. When we light it in the metric system, we do not assign any specific number (such as 1 meter) to the radius of its surrounding sphere. We pay attention instead to the solid angle (whose vertex is our candle) formed by the radius and a "square" section of the surface whose sides are equal to that radius. We call this solid angle a steradian. We should not be surprised to discover that there are 4π steradians in every sphere.

People who use metrics employ 1 lumen/steradian as their basic unit. They call this unit a candela.

If 1 lumen per square foot equals 1 footcandle, 1 lumen per square meter equals 1 lux. If the surface area is reduced to 1 cm^2, the unit becomes a phot. And 1 candela/m^2 is known as a nit.

If you recall that there are 10.76 ft^2 in 1m^2, you could extract foot Lamberts from candelas by dividing the latter by pi times the square feet (ftL=cd/πft^2).

Figure 6-1 shows graphically the basic light measuring terms for both the English and metric systems.

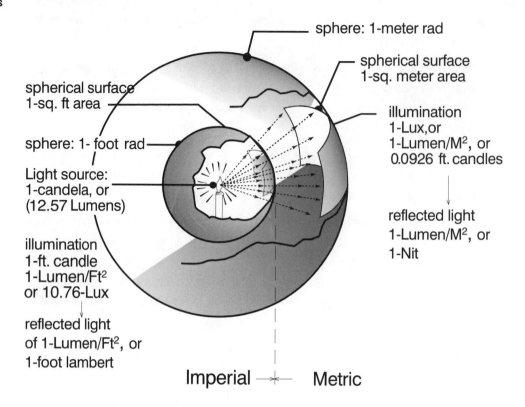

The scientific laws of light measurement
===

Three scientific laws govern light measurement. They are: the inverse square law, Lambert's cosine law and the cosine[4] law.

The inverse square law: The first and most intuitive, of course, is the inverse square law, which shows that one lumen of flux will spread out over an area that increases as the square of the distance from the center of the source. This means that the light per square foot decreases as the inverse square of the distance from that source.

There are some who conclude from this inverse square relationship that filling a screen from a greater throw distance affects image brightness differently than when the same screen is filled from a closer throw distance. But that is not so. Because the screen size is unchanged in both circumstances, we can see that the same amount of light is falling on it. Thus, as the projector is moved farther back from the screen its image size does not get larger because, presumably, we're using a lens with an appropriately longer focal length than we used in the short focal length case.

Note that if we don't change the focal length of the lens in Figure 6-2 and do double the distance, the image will become four times larger and one-fourth as bright.

FIG. 6-2

Inverse square law

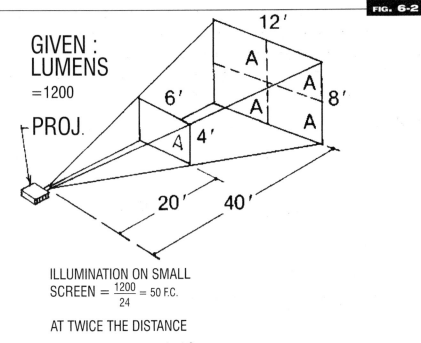

GIVEN :
LUMENS
=1200

PROJ.

ILLUMINATION ON SMALL
SCREEN = $\frac{1200}{24}$ = 50 F.C.

AT TWICE THE DISTANCE

ILLUMINATION $=50 \left(\frac{20}{40}\right)^2 = 12.5$ F.C.

LAW: DOUBLE THE DISTANCE-
$\frac{1}{4}$ THE ILLUMINATION $\left(\frac{1}{2}\right)^2 = \frac{1}{4}$

TRIPLE THE DISTANCE-
$\frac{1}{9}$ THE ILLUMINATION $\left(\frac{1}{3}\right)^2 = \frac{1}{9}$

Lambert's cosine law: This law states that the flux per unit solid angle in any direction from it varies as the cosine of the angle between that direction and the perpendicular to the transmitter (or reflector). It is used, therefore, to account for the obliquity of an angular ray striking a flat surface that is perpendicular to the optical axis of a light beam, as shown in Figure 6-3.

FIG. 6-3

Lambert's cosine law

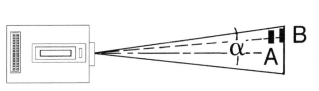

FT. CANDLES @ B = FC @ AX COS α
NOTE: LIGHT METER FACES LENS @ A.
LIGHT METER IS FLAT AGAINST
SCREEN @ B.

MEASURING LIGHT

The cosine⁴ law: This law takes into account the luminance (brightness) of the source, the resulting illumination on a normal (perpendicular) surface at a given distance, and the illumination at some point forming an angle α with the optical center. As illustrated in Figure 6-4, this law states that the footcandle reading at point B will be equal to the footcandle reading at point A multiplied by the 4th power of the cosine of the angle α.

Cosine⁴ law

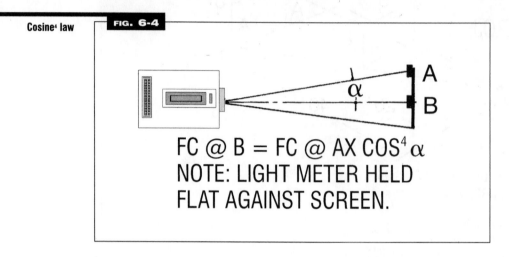

FIG. 6-4

$$FC\ @\ B = FC\ @\ A \times COS^4 \alpha$$
NOTE: LIGHT METER HELD
FLAT AGAINST SCREEN.

The cosine⁴ law also explains why, when a cone of light passes through the center of a lens, its intensity falls off toward the corners of a screen. This light fall-off is a fault neither of the lens nor of the screen; it is merely a law of physics at work.

7

PROJECTION

TECHNOLOGIES

written by **JODY THOMAS, CTS**

Jody Thomas, CTS, is CEO
of Kayye Consulting Inc., a
marketing and consulting
firm serving companies
in the professional
audiovisual industry.
He can be contacted at
jthomas@kayye.com.

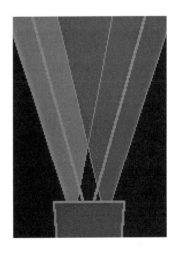

Projection technologies have been around since the creation of the film medium. In the early days of projection, transparent photographs were projected onto a flat white surface using a light bulb as an illumination source and a lens as the focusing mechanism. Conceptually, not much has changed from those days.

Since its inception, projection has taken a variety of forms for information sharing and entertainment. By slightly changing each photograph and then running each image in front of a light source, a perception of "motion pictures" became possible. Film projection has continued to evolve, but its basic format, an intense light source illuminating 24 pictures every second (24fps), has continued to dominate the entertainment industry.

Film projector

FIG. 7-1

COURTESY: VANIER COLLEGE, QUEBEC

With the advent of video, people wanted to display video and television images on a large projection screen. This was unimaginable to the creators of the television. When color television was created in the late 1940s, nobody imagined that there ever would be a need to display a video signal on a screen larger than 19 inches diagonally.

Then, as personal computers (PCs) became more prevalent in the business world and video projection technologies continued to develop, people wanted to display computer signals on a projector. Instead of text-based overhead transparencies, presenters discovered that they could use the computer to create transparencies and present them. Indeed, In the 1980s Harvard Graphics became the leading software application to the business presentation world because it enabled users to make "slide-show" style presentations electronically from PCs.

Harvard Graphics software allowed screen shots for electronically produced slide show presentations

FIG. 7-2

COURTESY: HARVARD GRAPHICS

More than 30 years old, electronic projection technology can be considered mature by many standards. Indeed, it has matured, but significant improvements continue to occur year after year. Until the early 1990s, almost every self-contained projector used for computer or video display required a technician for proper alignment. The alignment procedure might require two hours for a simple system, and eight hours or more for more complex systems. Only recently have projectors become simple enough for the average presenter to set up and operate with ease.

The basics of projection

How have these technologies evolved? It is important to understand some fundamentals about how projection systems function to comprehend the evolution. Projection systems require a projector, which consists of a light source, imaging device and focusing system. In some cases, the light source and imaging device are one and the same. Projection systems also require a smooth surface off which to reflect light or through which to transmit light. The systems operate within a projection environment, for better or for worse. In many cases, this is an environment shared by the viewers of the projection, and where the system and viewers have conflicting requirements.

FIG. 7-3   **Front projection screen**

COURTESY: DA-LITE SCREEN COMPANY

A fundamental of projection is that it falls within the physics of light transmission. Light from a projector is going to react consistently with any light source that exists in the environment. The same principles apply to projected light as to any light, including the way it reacts to air and to changes in media (air/glass/plastics), and its ability to reflect off, be absorbed by or transmit through obstacles it might encounter in a space. For the purposes of light transmission, we define black as the absence of light. Projectors cannot create black; this is a function of the environment in which the projection occurs. All projectors are considered additive devices, which means that they can only increase the light that would exist in an environment. In order for our eyes to perceive an image, we require only a difference between lightness and darkness. The difference between that lightness and darkness is perceived as contrast. The darkest possible intensity of a projection image is perceived as black, while the maximum amount of light a projector can muster is perceived as white.

Complicating matters is another characteristic of light. Black surfaces will absorb all colors of light, while white surfaces will reflect any color of light. This means that front projection screens must be white for the projected image to be seen, while rear screens must be dark (yet translucent) so that contrast becomes possible. Since projection screens are passive devices, they cannot distinguish between what is projected and what is naturally occurring ambient light.

The term *system black* refers to the naturally occurring light that is reflected or transmitted on or through a screen, prior to the addition of any projected light. Since no projection environment is perfectly absent of light, there always will be a deficiency in projection contrast. The lower the ambient light on the screen, the better the projection contrast. A very bright projector can overcome significant ambient light. Any projector can perform well in relative darkness and still create excellent contrast.

Projector fundamentals compared and contrasted

As projection technologies have evolved, new advantages have been introduced. But with every advantage comes a tradeoff in other potentially critical areas. There are three fundamental characteristics of electronic projection systems that differentiate performance and capabilities: image creation, illumination and color creation. Let's consider each of them.

Image creation: To create an image, a projector relies on some method of accepting an electronic video signal, then reproducing that signal on an imaging device. Imaging devices process this video information in one of two ways: by scanning the image onto the imaging device, or through the illumination of specific pixels in a matrix array.

Scanning image creation

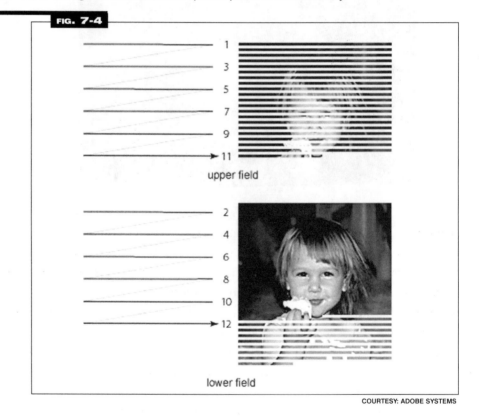

FIG. 7-4

upper field

lower field

COURTESY: ADOBE SYSTEMS

Scanning-based systems. Scanning methodology is similar to what a television does to create an image. By starting at the top left of the image, scanning left to right, then beginning again on the next row, the scanning-based imaging system creates pictures as the elements of the picture in each row are illuminated, and then disappear. By quickly drawing a picture 30 or more times per second, it creates moving electronic pictures. The advantage of a scanning-based imaging system is that it is extremely flexible in its ability to respond to different types of signals. It is equivalent to a painter with a canvas on which to paint a portrait; it can apply to almost any "paint." There are few specific limitations in the way that the image can be scanned. The system is capable of handling interlaced video or progressive video without conversion of the signal. The picture element can be sized easily according to the signal requirements. The overall picture shape also is not defined; geometric distortions may be used to correct an image in specialized applications.

An advantage and drawback to scanning-based systems is their ability to support various refresh rates, or the number of images drawn per second. The advantage is that this support provides wide compatibility with a variety of video signals, whether they are operating at 60Hz, 72Hz or 120Hz. The projector simply scans each image faster with the increase in refresh rate. The drawback of this technology is that viewers of an image with a relatively low refresh rate often perceive a certain amount of flicker in the image, similar to that within a computer monitor. Flicker is often perceived as high as 60Hz under specific lighting conditions. By increasing the refresh rate, the perception of flicker disappears.

Another drawback to scanning-based systems is that there is little definition between the vertical picture elements, which results in a "softer" perceived image when viewing computer images, which are composed of clearly defined horizontal and vertical picture elements. In addition, with lower pixel resolution video signals, there can be too much definition between the horizontal rows of pixels. The black spacing created by this definition is perceived as scan lines; this may be distracting, especially with traditional video signals. By increasing the scanning frequency using a "line doubling" or "line quadrupling" device, the definition of the scan lines is reduced, providing an overall film-like image.

FIG. 7-5

COURTESY: KAYYE CONSULTING

Effects of a line doubler on a scanned image

A matrix array of pixels. The alternative to scanning-based systems is a matrix array of pixels. Similar in concept to the Light Brite™ child's toy, the matrix array of pixels illuminates a fixed array of aligned horizontal and vertical pixels to create a picture. Each pixel represents a single picture element, and can be turned on and off. By using enough pixels in rows and columns, the perception of an image can be created. Increasing the intensity of each pixel's illumination or the amount of time it remains "on" can make the pixel appear brighter. Eliminating the light transmitted from the pixel has the effect of an absence of light.

A key advantage of this method of image creation is the ability to create an image using clearly defined horizontal rows and vertical columns. By clearly defining each picture element individually, the image is perceived as clearer than that of a scanning system image.

FIG. 7-6

COURTESY: KAYYE CONSULTING

The matrix array of pixels also happens to be its key drawback. Unlike scanning systems, which create the resolution required by the video signal, all matrix-based systems have a fixed array of picture elements called the native resolution. This means that a projected image will appear most accurate if the video resolution directly corresponds to the native resolution of the projector. For instance, if a display has 1,024 columns of pixels and 768 rows of pixels, then it will appear most accurate if the video source being displayed also has a resolution of 1,024x768 pixels (XGA). It is indeed possible to display alternate resolutions on a projection display. However these images must be processed electronically if they are to occupy the exact area of the imaging device. For instance, when fed into a projector with a native resolution of 1,024x768 pixels, a video source occupying 800x600 pixels must be stretched to fit the entire area of the 1,024x768 matrix array, since it contains approximately 39 percent less picture information. When fed into the same 1024x768 projector, a video source occupying 1,600x1,200 pixels must be compressed to fit the area of the 1,024x768 array, since it contains almost 2.5 times the amount of picture information.

The electronic device used to process the information is called a scaler. Most projectors incorporate a scaler to provide compatibility with non-native resolution video signals. This device analyzes each pixel's information and determines how to expand that information to address multiple pixels in the case of expansion, or get rid of excess information in the case of compression. Early scalers were very limited in their ability to process this information. They would compress an image by eliminating entire rows and columns of pixel information, causing a very choppy image that evidently lacked information. Now that scaling technology has improved, scalers can run complex algorithms to determine what the new pixel information should "look like." The result is images with little apparent loss of pixel information. Some matrix-based displays also now take on characteristics of scanning-based displays, whereby the image can be distorted geometrically on the matrix array for the purpose of image correction; in this case, some of the pixels simply aren't used.

Another factor in creation of an image using a matrix-based system is that all pixel information within a frame of video is created at the same time. All information from the entire frame is "read" into a buffer, then all pixel information is displayed simultaneously. There is no advantage to using increased refresh rates with a matrix-based system; there is no perception of flicker that is created as a result of the refresh rate.

All matrix-based systems can be regarded as digital in the method they use to divide and represent pixel information. This means that each supported resolution must be programmed into the projector, limiting the projector to display video signals in which a pre-programmed resolution exists. Most projector manufacturers program in a wide range of standard resolutions, including multiple refresh rates at each resolution. Some projectors can support newly created resolutions through firmware upgrades or user programming. There also is no support for interlaced images in a matrix-based display; these video signals must be "de-interlaced" prior to pixel addressing.

An example of a fixed-matrix display technology is the LCD (liquid crystal display) monitor or projector.

The illumination system: The second key component of a projector is its illumination system. This system determines how bright the projected image will be, as well as how much contrast an image may contain. There are three basic methods of providing image illumination: emissive, transmissive and reflective.

Emissive illumination. In an emissive illumination system, the device that generates the image also generates the light used for illumination. The device emanates light from the picture elements and focuses this light through a lens, which creates the picture on a screen. This is the only method of illumination in which theoretically perfect black can be created. Since black is created by the absence of light, then perfect black is only possible if the light source is completely removed for the specific pixel information.

A significant limitation of emissive systems is that potential brightness of an image is tied directly to the technology implementation. There is no method of increasing light output without changing the technology implementation. In addition, there is a direct correlation between image detail and brightness in an emissive system; with an increase in brightness comes a loss of image detail, and with continued increases in brightness the image eventually will become unusable, as each picture element breaks down and loses its ability to create light and detail simultaneously. With emissive systems, the lower the light output, the greater the image detail.

Transmissive illumination. The second method of illumination is the transmission of an intense "white" light source through a translucent resolution-generating device. With this method, the light source and resolution-generating device are entirely separate systems. The light source is always on when the projector is on. The capability of the projector to create contrast is determined by the resolution-generating device's ability to block light within each picture element. The more light that is allowed to pass through each picture element, the brighter the resulting image becomes. Generally the light source used in a transmissive system is some type of lamp assembly, which provides a very intense light source.

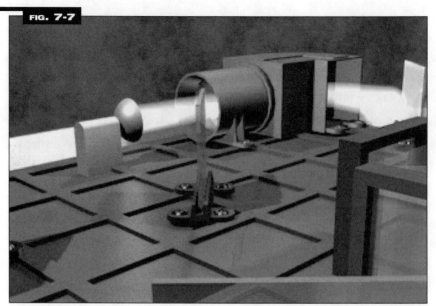

FIG. 7-7

COURTESY: KAYYE CONSULTING

One of the side effects of transmissive systems is heating of the resolution-generating device. There are two primary contributors to light output in a transmissive system. One is the light output potential of a system before heat from the light source damages the resolution-generating device or components. The second is the efficiency of the resolution-generating device in passing light. The greater the efficiency, the more light will pass through the transmissive resolution-generating device and ultimately reach the screen.

Generally, transmissive systems use a matrix-based resolution-generating device. Light passing through this device may pass through the pixel or may impact the spaces between the pixels, which results in lost light (as the space between pixels is made up of wires in a display like an LCD). The larger the pixel area, the more efficiency the system will have in passing light. As the native resolution of the imaging device increases, the pixel size decreases, provided that the overall aperture of the imaging device remains the same, thus decreasing the efficiency of its ability to pass light.

Another effect of a separate light source is that the color spectrum reproduced on the projection screen is heavily dependent on the light spectrum available from the light source. If the light emitted from the light source is yellowish (such as light from a halogen lamp-based projector), then all light projected will be yellowish. This also applies to the uniformity of light distribution. The light source used in projection systems must be very uniform in light output; otherwise "hotspots" of intensity will appear on the projection screen. Transmissive systems are very susceptible to this characteristic; slight variations in density of the transmissive resolution-generating device can cause varying efficiencies in its ability to pass light.

Reflective illumination. The third method of illumination is the reflection of a light source off of a reflective resolution-generating device. Like transmissive systems, the light source and resolution-generating device are entirely separate, and the light source remains on when the projector is on. In reflective systems, when light is reflected off of the resolution-generating device and out through the lens, projected light is created. When the reflective device blocks light or deflects light away from the lens, the perception of black is created. Different reflective technologies use different methods to create this perception of black.

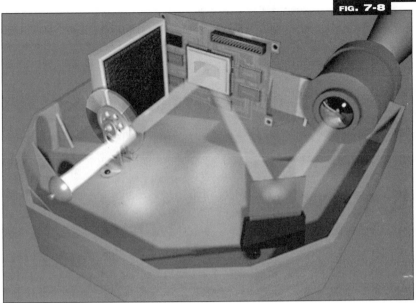

FIG. 7-8

Reflective illumination system

COURTESY: KAYYE CONSULTING

The advantage of reflective systems is that light no longer has to pass through the imaging device. As with transmissive systems, light output potential is determined by the amount of light available from the light source and the reflective device's efficiency at reflecting the light. Also, as with transmissive systems, the reflective device is susceptible to heat from the light source, but it generally is more resilient to these effects.

The overall surface area of the reflective device and the area occupied by the picture elements determines the device's efficiency. With a transmissive system, as the resolution increases the light efficiency of the projector decreases. With a reflective system, the opposite is true. As the resolution increases, the efficiency of the device at reflecting light also increases. Since reflective systems also use an independent light source, they are susceptible to the same color and intensity characteristics of the light source.

Creation of color in a projection system

All of the resolution-generating systems discussed can produce only monochrome (or black and white) images. Color is created in projection systems the same way it is created in television displays: the additive combination of red, green and blue pixel information is used to create the color spectrum that the human eye can perceive. The absence of all three colors creates the perception of black. The combination of all three colors in the proper proportions can be used to create any color, including "white."

The video signals sent to a projector are composed of color information. In the case of computer signals, the video is composed of red, green and blue picture information, along with the necessary synchronization information that tells the projector how the information should appear. In the case of an encoded video signal, such as composite video or component, the color video signal must first be decoded when it is received at the projector. A decoder converts these encoded signals into the red, green, blue and synchronization components.

The simplest way to create color in a projection system is through the combination of three separate resolution-generating devices of equal resolution capabilities. Each device is responsible for creation of picture information for each of the three primary colors.

Then these three projected images are recombined to create the color image that appears on the projection screen. This recombination process is called convergence. There are three types of convergence systems: internally converged, externally converged and pre-converged.

The internally converged system: In an internally converged color system, the three independent resolution-generating devices are combined through an optical system before the light leaves the projector through the lens. This means that an internally converged projector requires only a single lens through which all light simultaneously passes. Provided that all three resolution-generating devices stay in proper optical alignment with each other, the image always will be properly converged, so that the red, green and blue picture elements will overlay each other perfectly when viewed in the projected image. Slight movement of the red optical path in relation to green and blue causes red mis-convergence, where a slight separation is viewed between the red picture element information and its corresponding green and blue picture element information.

Internally converged color system

FIG. 7-9

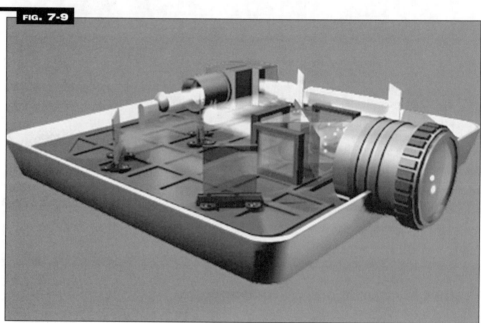

COURTESY: KAYYE CONSULTING

The advantage of an internally converged color system is that the convergence can be done by the projector manufacturer in the assembly process, and does not have to be performed by the user unless mis-convergence ensues at a later time. This lends itself well to "point-and-shoot" projection systems that require little setup for proper operation. Any effect of zooming or focusing the projection lens will not affect the convergence of the imaging devices.

The drawback of an internally converged system is the complexity of the internal optical path that light must follow. An internally converged system requires an array of mirrors and prisms to control the direction and recombination of light before it leaves the lens. This complex optical system occupies space, although the space can be miniaturized to a significant degree.

The externally converged system: The second type of convergence system is externally converged. In this system, the projector includes three separate resolution-generating devices, each of which has its own optical path and lens. Convergence of the image does not occur until the image reaches the screen. In this scenario, the projector is projecting three entirely independent images that must be converged for proper operation.

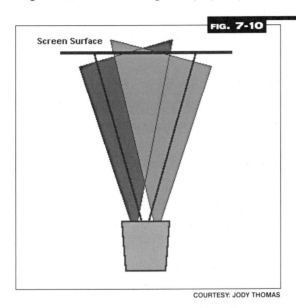

FIG. 7-10

Screen Surface

COURTESY: JODY THOMAS

Externally converged color system

In an internally converged projector, the single lens is designed to operate "on-axis" with the projection screen, which means that the projector and lens are perfectly perpendicular horizontally in relationship to the screen surface. In an externally converged projector, only one of the three lenses may be on-axis with the screen. (Generally this would be the green, dominant color). The flanking red and blue lenses adjacent the green are turned slightly inward so that the red and blue images overlay the green perfectly. This slight inward angle, however, is dependent on the distance between the projection lenses and the screen surface. The inward angle will differ depending on whether the screen is 100 inches or 250 inches from the lenses. The greater the distance to the projection screen, the smaller the inward angle of the flanking lenses.

If the angle of the flanking lenses is too great, horizontal mis-convergence of the red and blue images in relation to green can ensue, and each image will take on geometric shaping characteristics different from those of the other images. While a green image on-axis with the projection screen may take on a perfectly rectangular shape, the flanking images, when projected at a slight horizontal angle, will appear to have one side slightly greater in height than the other. This is referred to as horizontal keystoning. A projection lens angled slightly right-to-left will have a greater height on the left side of the image than on the right side, as the distance between the lens and the left side of the image is greater than that of the lens and the right side of the image. The slightest variation of angle can make significant differences in the positioning and geometric shape of each image, thus all externally converged projectors incorporate geometric shaping capabilities to pre-compensate for distortions created by the lens angles.

Overlaying multiple images at a relatively great distance is quite challenging. Obtaining identical geometric shapes, illumination and focus with accuracy at a fraction of an image on a proportionately large screen area requires expertise and time. Few automated systems have been developed that are able to account for the variances that exist in each application. Slight movement of the projector in relation to the screen can cause new, significant differences between the images, resulting in a new alignment procedure.

Why incorporate external convergence into a projector, with all of these complications? The reasons are that certain resolution-generation technologies operate much more efficiently with external convergence, and that the optics internal to the projector are much simpler than those in an internally converged system. Great flexibility in the adjustment procedure of each image helps to overcome the complications of an externally converged system.

For example, an externally converged system would allow one to display an image that is amorphous in shape (an image with bent corners, for example, or one projected on an unusually shaped screen or even on water).

The pre-converged system: The last type of convergence system is pre-converged, that is, a single imaging device generates all three primary colors. A pre-converged system might use a three-layer resolution-generating device to accomplish this, or a sequential color system that alternates the light applied to the resolution-generating device. Since convergence is not necessary or takes place within the imaging device, the complexity of setup in an externally converged system and the complexity of the optical path in an internally converged system are avoided. Also avoided is the potential for mis-convergence within the projector.

Choosing the pre-converged system brings benefits as well as tradeoffs of other technological capabilities.

Pre-converged color system (multi-layer)

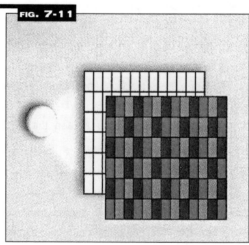

FIG. 7-11

COURTESY: KAYYE CONSULTING

Technology implementation

Now we have a fundamental understanding of how a projected image is created. Although certain image creation, illumination and color creation methods dominate today's projection marketplace, new technologies are under development constantly, and the various methods for creating a projected image are being revisited. Table 7-1 summarizes the technology implementation currently available in the marketplace.

TABLE 7-1 Technology implementation summary

TECHNOLOGY	IMAGE CREATION	ILLUMINATION	COLOR CREATION
CRT projection	Scanning	Emissive	Externally converged
LCD	Matrix	Transmissive*	Internally converged
Single-chip DLP™	Matrix	Reflective	Pre-converged
Three-chip DLP™	Matrix	Reflective	Internally converged
ILA light valve	Scanning	Reflective *	Externally converged
LCOS	Matrix	Reflective	Internally converged
Laser projection	Matrix	Reflective	Internally converged

* Denotes most common implementation.
  Other implementations may use alternative color creation methods.

The basis of CRT projection

Cathode Ray Tube (CRT) projection technology, developed in the early 1970s, was the first pre-dominant video projection technology. One of the first efforts was the Advent Videobeam developed by Henry Kloss, also the founder of Cambridge Sound Works. Although some of the first CRT projectors varied in implementation, a vast majority have followed similar principles since those early days.

FIG. 7-12   **Advent videobeam**

COURTESY: ADVENT VIDEO CORPORATION

Basically, a CRT projector contains three monochromatic CRTs with different colored phosphors on the inside of a clear glass face. To understand the operation of a CRT projector requires a basic understanding of how a CRT creates an image. High voltage delivers a stream of electrons down the neck of a vacuum tube, and these electrons strike the face of the tube with great energy. Light is created when the electron stream strikes the phosphorous coating the inside the face of the tube. To control the intense stream of electrons, an electromagnetic deflection coil is employed around the neck of the tube. By varying the magnetic field, the place where the electron stream strikes the phosphors can be controlled. By quickly moving the stream of electrons across the face of the tube, a picture can be created.

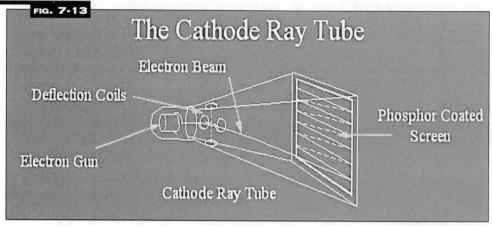

FIG. 7-13

The Cathode Ray Tube

Deflection Coils

Electron Beam

Electron Gun

Phosphor Coated Screen

Cathode Ray Tube

COURTESY: KAYYE CONSULTING

In a CRT projector, each of the three picture tubes employs a different colored phosphorous surface, so that the light created on each tube will represent one of the three primary colors. Since each image is monochromatic, only the relevant color information is fed to the picture tube. (Red information is delivered to the red picture tube, and so on.)

There are several differences between the CRTs used in these projectors and today's televisions. First, televisions must create color within one picture tube. To do this, red, green and blue phosphors are applied to the area for each picture element, so that color can be created with each picture element on the face of the tube. To control where the stream of electrons creates each picture element, a shadow mask, or metal sheet with an array of holes, is employed within the picture tube. Electrons will only pass through the holes, so there are relatively tight controls over which phosphors are illuminated at which times. Secondly, the intensity of light from a CRT projection tube is substantially greater than that in the television, since the light from the tube must illuminate the image on a screen. To accomplish this illumination, the force at which the electron stream strikes the phosphorous surface is much greater in a CRT projector picture tube, and the size of the picture tube is smaller than generally would be used in a television. CRT projector picture tubes generally range in size from 6 to 9 inches diagonally. Tubes much smaller than 6 inches diagonally do not produce enough light for projection, and tubes much larger than 9 inches diagonally require lenses of such weight that they become impractical to manufacture.

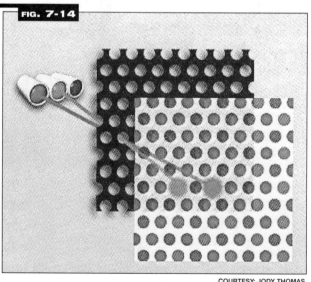

FIG. 7-14

COURTESY: JODY THOMAS

CRT projection has several key benefits inherent to the technologies it employs. First, CRT projectors are very flexible in their ability to support various signal types and re-create various images through the scanning process of image creation, which yields great flexibility and very high-resolution support. Modern CRT projectors have the ability to create images in excess of 3,000 x 3,000 pixels of resolution, and are the only projection systems that work for very high resolution, specific applications. Since the CRT projector scanning process allows great flexibility, images can be reshaped as necessary for the most extreme screen shapes and projection angles.

Second, CRT projectors do an excellent job of creating black through the absence of light. Since CRT projectors employ an emissive technology, the electron stream is momentarily "turned off" to create the absence of light, or black.

Third, through an external convergence system, complete control over how the images align allows great flexibility in the applications of CRT projectors. Although the alignment procedure for external convergence is complex, opting for an internally converged system would mean a loss of extremely valuable light output and an increase in mass.

The drawbacks of CRT projection technology became very evident during the boom of the business computer presentation. They include insufficient light output, long setup time and substantial weight. These factors have all but eliminated CRT projection from mainstream commercial use in computer presentations, although CRT systems continue to dominate in certain segments of commercial and home cinema applications.

The insufficient light output is a result of the emissive method of illumination employed by CRT projector picture tubes. As light output increases, the size of the beam spot—the area of illumination on a picture element—increases. High-resolution signals require a very small beam spot size for sufficient detail to enable viewers to recognize the picture element as a pixel of information. If the beam spot size is too large, the picture information becomes fuzzy. If the light output becomes too great, the phosphor loses its ability to control the beam spot size, and streaking of the specific color light ensues.

FIG. 7-15

Streaking example

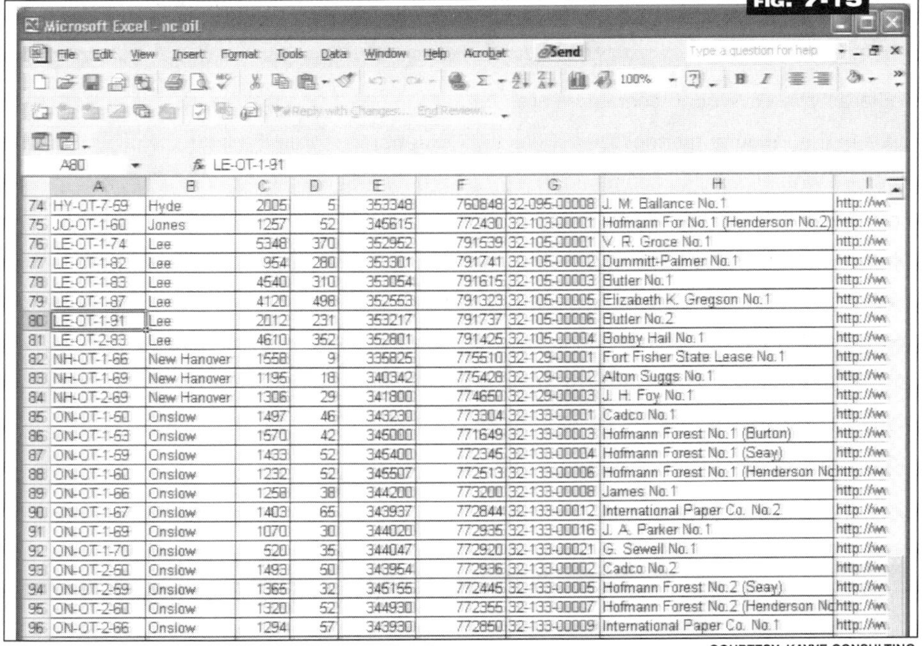

	A	B	C	D	E	F	G	H	I
74	HY-OT-7-59	Hyde	2005	5	353348	760848	32-095-00008	J. M. Ballance No. 1	http://ww
75	JO-OT-1-60	Jones	1257	52	345615	772430	32-103-00001	Hofmann For No. 1 (Henderson No. 2)	http://ww
76	LE-OT-1-74	Lee	5348	370	352952	791539	32-105-00001	V. R. Groce No. 1	http://ww
77	LE-OT-1-82	Lee	954	280	353301	791741	32-105-00002	Dummitt-Palmer No. 1	http://ww
78	LE-OT-1-83	Lee	4540	310	353054	791615	32-105-00003	Butler No. 1	http://ww
79	LE-OT-1-87	Lee	4120	498	352553	791323	32-105-00005	Elizabeth K. Gregson No. 1	http://ww
80	LE-OT-1-91	Lee	2012	231	353217	791737	32-105-00006	Butler No. 2	http://ww
81	LE-OT-2-83	Lee	4610	352	352801	791425	32-105-00004	Bobby Hall No. 1	http://ww
82	NH-OT-1-66	New Hanover	1558	9	335825	775510	32-129-00001	Fort Fisher State Lease No. 1	http://ww
83	NH-OT-1-69	New Hanover	1195	18	340342	775428	32-129-00002	Alton Suggs No. 1	http://ww
84	NH-OT-2-69	New Hanover	1306	29	341800	774650	32-129-00003	J. H. Foy No. 1	http://ww
85	ON-OT-1-50	Onslow	1497	46	343230	773304	32-133-00001	Cadco No. 1	http://ww
86	ON-OT-1-53	Onslow	1570	42	345000	771649	32-133-00003	Hofmann Forest No. 1 (Burton)	http://ww
87	ON-OT-1-59	Onslow	1433	52	345400	772345	32-133-00004	Hofmann Forest No. 1 (Seay)	http://ww
88	ON-OT-1-60	Onslow	1232	52	345507	772513	32-133-00006	Hofmann Forest No. 1 (Henderson No	http://ww
89	ON-OT-1-66	Onslow	1258	38	344200	773200	32-133-00008	James No. 1	http://ww
90	ON-OT-1-67	Onslow	1403	65	343937	772844	32-133-00012	International Paper Co. No. 2	http://ww
91	ON-OT-1-69	Onslow	1070	30	344020	772935	32-133-00016	J. A. Parker No. 1	http://ww
92	ON-OT-1-70	Onslow	520	35	344047	772920	32-133-00021	G. Sewell No. 1	http://ww
93	ON-OT-2-50	Onslow	1493	50	343954	772936	32-133-00002	Cadco No. 2	http://ww
94	ON-OT-2-59	Onslow	1365	32	345155	772445	32-133-00005	Hofmann Forest No. 2 (Seay)	http://ww
95	ON-OT-2-60	Onslow	1320	52	344930	772355	32-133-00007	Hofmann Forest No. 2 (Henderson No	http://ww
96	ON-OT-2-66	Onslow	1294	57	343930	772650	32-133-00009	International Paper Co. No. 1	http://ww

PROJECTION TECHNOLOGIES

Another effect of this emissive technology is that electrons strike the center of the picture tube with greater force than those that strike the sides and corners of the picture tube. The result is an image that is brighter in the center than on the sides and edges. The difference in intensity may be as great as 70 percent, depending on the size of the picture tube and implementation. Although human eyes have a tendency to "forgive" this difference in intensity, the resultant measurements are very unforgiving.

This emissive technology also affects the system's efficiency in control of brightness. The smaller the area of illumination to create a projected image, the brighter the image will be. Since most projected video images are composed of small areas of intensity rather than large areas of great intensity, picture tubes can work very efficiently at directing light energy to the smaller areas. When a picture consists of a wider aspect ratio than that of the picture tubes, energy is directed only to the areas in use.

ANSI left; Peak right

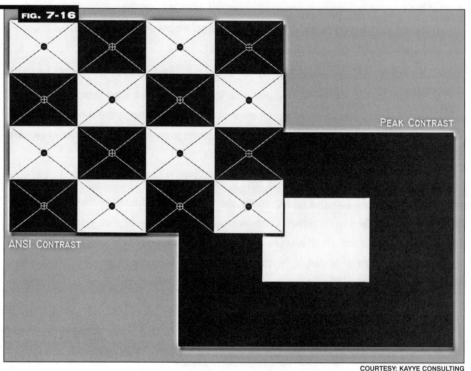

FIG. 7-16

PEAK CONTRAST

ANSI CONTRAST

COURTESY: KAYYE CONSULTING

Two different measurement techniques are needed in order to compare CRT projector light output with that of other technologies. Peak light output measures the intensity of projected light on a screen when the light is confined to a small area. ANSI measurements represent average intensity when the entire available image area is illuminated. In modern CRT projectors, it is not uncommon for the projector to have a measurement rating of 1,200 or more peak lumens, but an ANSI measurement of 250 ANSI lumens. The most advanced CRT projectors are able to muster only 300 ANSI lumens, which is relatively dim compared with other technologies. With other technologies, the peak and ANSI measurements are one and the same; there are no efficiency gains realized by a reduction in the size of the projected image area. With these technologies, the light simply is lost when the image size is reduced.

As development of CRT projectors occurred, new ways to maximize light output were discovered, many of which dealt with the ability to minimize light refraction in the optical system of each CRT and lens system. One method of minimizing refraction was to alter the optical systems to include a mix of glass and plastic elements. Another method involved removing the air space between the CRT face and the first element of the lens. By filling this space with glycol, a liquid with a refractive index similar to that of glass, refraction is minimized.

Another limitation in CRT projection was that, unlike other technologies, it was not suitable for use with variable focal length (zoom) lenses. With the introduction of additional lens elements, the additional refraction resulted in light loss. Also, the lenses represented a significant increase in weight, so that the cost of gaining additional abilities in projector placement was too great.

FIG. 7-17

Setup pattern

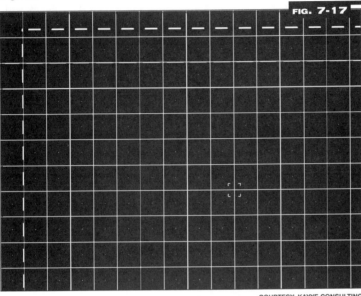

COURTESY: KAYYE CONSULTING

In early projection systems, all of the signals that would be displayed were of relatively low resolution. Some form of encoded video or RGB (red, green, blue) video represented these signals. These early projectors were designed to operate at a fixed scan rate (15.75kHz), with a fixed refresh rate (29.97Hz) in an interlaced signal format. Since these requirements were consistent with most of the video signals used in modern video, there was no need for the CRT projector to be compatible with more than this one signal. But as computer video standards developed, it became necessary to address these higher scan rates, refresh rates and signal formats. As VGA video became the predominant computer video standard in the mid 1980s, it was necessary for CRT projectors to be compatible with a greater number of signal types. And as the signals increased in scan rate and refresh rate, the adjustment procedures that were acceptable for single scan rate projectors became inadequate.

FIG. 7-18

Digital projector remote

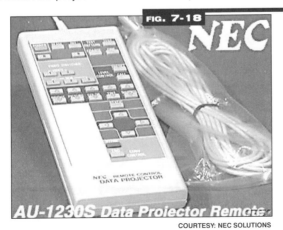

AU-1230S Data Projector Remote

COURTESY: NEC SOLUTIONS

A great advancement in CRT projectors was development of the ability to control the impact of the electron stream on the face of the picture tube. In the early projectors, controls were somewhat limited to rudimentary adjustments that allowed for positioning of an image, height, width and other basic positioning. These adjustments were accomplished through the use of a screwdriver and potentiometers on the high voltage deflection board within the projector. As the adjustment capabilities expanded, greater and greater control over the deflection became possible, allowing more and more precise adjustments. One of the greatest advancements in CRT projection was development of the ability to perform adjustments digitally, which allowed an operator to set up the projector using a remote control, and then store the settings in nonvolatile memory within the projector. Once they were stored, these settings could be recalled for the various signals that might be fed to the projector.

Another advancement that came about as a result of higher resolution signals was the ability to improve the focus of an image optically and electronically. To focus the image optically, the projector provides an overall and edge focus adjustment for each lens. To optimize the image, it also became necessary to adjust the gap between the CRT face and the first element of the lens. This is referred to as the Scheimpflug adjustment, after Theodor Scheimpflug of Austria (even though the adjustment was patented by Jules Carpentier of Paris in 1901 for still camera systems). By modifying the distance relationship between the face of the CRT and the first element of the lens, focus can be improved dramatically.

Scheimpflug adjustment

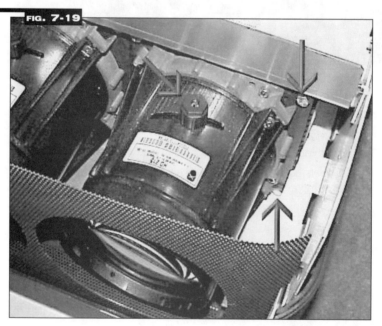

FIG. 7-19

COURTESY: ZENITH ELECTRONICS

Electronic focus advancements were called dynamic focus. This refers to the ability to distort the shape of the beam spot, depending on the area where the electron stream strikes the phosphor. If the electron stream were striking a corner of the picture tube, the stream would hit at an angle, causing an oval-shaped beam spot. Pre-distorting the beam spot into an opposite oval would create a round beam spot.

A final drawback in current CRT projection technology has not been overcome, and is inherent to the technology. An electron stream can energize the phosphorous materials used inside the CRT face for only a limited time. After the phosphors are energized to create light, they will start to decay over time. The longer they are illuminated, the sooner they will decay. Uneven decay between phosphor areas through the display of a still image for an extended period of time results in what is known as "burn-in." In burn-in, a "shadow" of an image remains after the image is removed. Once burn-in has occurred, it is not possible to reverse the effect. Burning all of the phosphors on the picture tube for an extended period of time can minimize the appearance of burn-in; however this shortens the life span of the tube.

In applications that require still images for an extended period of time, it is necessary to incorporate technology that slowly rotates the image so that the intensity of the illumination is spread over an area. This extends the life of the picture tubes. The rate of burn-in is dependent on several factors, including the intensity of the electron stream against the phosphors and the scan rate of the incoming signal. Burn-in can occur, though, in as short a time as 8 to 10 hours.

FIG. 7-20   **Effect of burn-in**

COURTESY: KAYYE CONSULTING

The basis of LCD projection

LCD led an evolutionary storm in projection technology in the late 1980s and early 1990s. First came the invention of the self-contained LCD video projector in 1989. The projector was able to display video images using its internal lamp and array of three LCD panels. This revolutionary device transformed the projection marketplace by making quick and easy projector setup a reality.

Shortly after invention of the self-contained LCD projector came invention of the LCD projection panel, a device designed to display computer graphics. Using the lamp and optics of an overhead projector, this device sat on top of an overhead projector stage and was connected to a computer video port. The device transformed portable presentation from the transparency-based print world to the electronic age. Although CRT projectors were capable of displaying computer graphics, it was impractical for mobile presenters to transport or allow the necessary setup time. The first LCD projection panels were capable of displaying only grayscale images; however these devices quickly were accepted as the future of business presentations.

FIG. 7-21   **Self- contained LCD projector**

COURTESY: SHARP ELECTRONICS

As LCD projection panels continued to improve, color and video were incorporated, allowing greater flexibility and polish in business presentations. The reign of the LCD projection panel would be short-lived, however, as many manufacturers were focused on the incorporation of computer display technology into self-contained LCD projectors. This occurred in 1993, and the rapid evolutionary pace continued for many years as the technology matured.

Kodak datashow LCD panel

FIG. 7-22

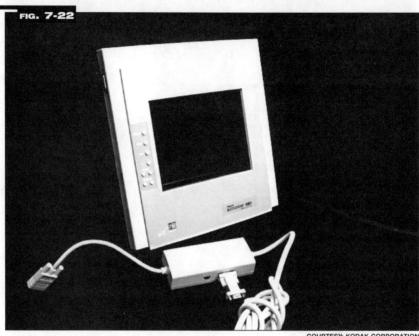

COURTESY: KODAK CORPORATION

The LCD technology incorporated into these early displays, and into the displays known today, relies on the same fundamentals. A light source is transmitted through a matrix-based display system, and the resultant light is passed through a lens to the projection screen. A vast majority of LCD projectors relies on internally converged systems, while a few implementations have relied on pre-converged systems, using filters applied to monochromatic LCD panels.

To understand this technology, it is important to understand how light is passed and blocked within an LCD pixel. Liquid crystals in their native state are random in order. Each pixel within an LCD panel contains a significant number of these liquid crystals. Single axis, polarized light enters the pixel, and if the liquid crystals are in their native random state, the light will "twist" and pass through the pixel. If an electric charge is applied to the pixel, though, the liquid crystals will orient themselves in an ordered fashion, which prevents the polarized light from twisting. If the polarized light cannot twist, it cannot pass through the pixel. The result is a perceived absence of light in that pixel. The amount of light that is allowed to pass through the pixel determines the relative intensity of the pixel at that time. By allowing light to pass through some pixels and be blocked by others, an image is created in the LCD panel.

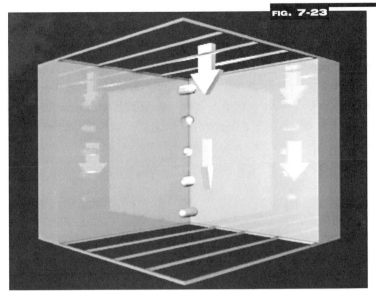

COURTESY: KAYYE CONSULTING

Addressing pixels in an LCD

An early and key differentiator between LCD implementations was how each pixel was addressed to provide the voltage. Many early implementations relied on a passive matrix system, which uses a simple grid to supply the charge to a particular pixel on the display. The grid is formed by two glass layers called substrates; one substrate is given columns and the other is given rows made from a transparent conductive material.

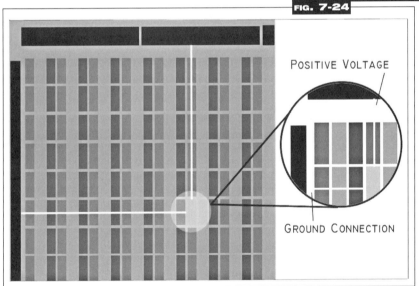

POSITIVE VOLTAGE

GROUND CONNECTION

COURTESY: KAYYE CONSULTING

Each row and column is connected to an integrated circuit that controls when a charge is sent down that column or row. The liquid crystal material is sandwiched between the substrates, and a polarizing film is added to the outer side of the substrates, oriented opposite each other. To turn on a pixel, the integrated circuit sends a charge down the correct column of one substrate and a ground on the correct row of the other. The row and column intersect at the designated pixel, and that delivers the voltage to untwist the liquid crystals at that pixel. The polarized light passes through the first polarized film, and if the light twists in the pixel then it also will pass through the opposite polarized film and on through the lens.

Drawbacks to passive matrix technology

There are some significant drawbacks to passive matrix technology. The primary drawbacks are relatively slow response time and imprecise voltage control. The response time refers to the LCD's ability to refresh the image displayed. Low response time causes the resulting image to appear to streak with quick movement. Imprecise voltage control hinders the passive matrix's ability to influence only one pixel at a time. When voltage is applied to untwist one pixel, the pixels around it also untwist partially, which can make images appear fuzzy and lack contrast.

Active matrix addressing

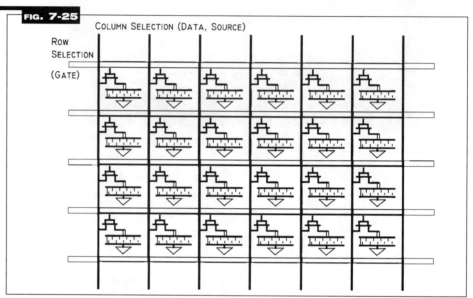

FIG. 7-25

COLUMN SELECTION (DATA, SOURCE)

ROW SELECTION (GATE)

COURTESY: KAYYE CONSULTING

Active matrix implementations do not have this problem. Active matrix addressing depends on thin film transistors (TFT), which are tiny switching transistors and capacitors. They are arranged in a matrix on a glass substrate. To address a particular pixel, the proper row is switched on, and then a charge is sent down the correct column. In active matrix addressing, all of the other rows that the column intersects are turned off, and only the capacitor at the designated pixel receives a charge. The capacitor is able to hold the charge until the next refresh cycle. Careful control of the amount of voltage supplied to a pixel will allow it to untwist only enough to let some light pass through. By applying this control in very small increments, it is possible to obtain 256 shades of gray per pixel.

Polysilicon substrates

The next big advancement in LCD technology came in the mid-1990s with the introduction of polysilicon substrates. Prior to this time, glass substrates were most common, and they required a relatively large aperture. In 640x480 resolution projectors, use of polysilicon substrates reduced the required size of the LCD panels from approximately 3 inches diagonally to 1.3 inches diagonally. This advancement reduced the entire size of the optical path significantly, thus reducing the overall size necessary for the projector. With increased efficiencies in use of polysilicon substrates, the efficiency of the panel in its ability to pass light also increased, as was evidenced in the Epson ELP-3000 projector, one of the first to make use of polysilicon LCD panels.

FIG. 7-26

COURTESY: EPSON AMERICA

Although some implementations of projectors use a single, filtered LCD panel to produce color, this has been the exception rather than the norm. These projectors have not been able to produce sufficient contrast to be comparable to three-panel LCD systems. Today, three-panel LCD projectors dominate in LCD projection technology.

In a three-panel LCD system, light leaves a lamp assembly and passes through several filters to rid itself of unwanted ultraviolet and infrared light. It then goes through a polarization process. In early polarization processes, light that was not polarized correctly would simply be filtered off, leaving a small fraction of the light available to create the image. As light polarization developed, polarizing prisms became commonplace. These would recapture un-polarized light and reorient it so that it became usable.

FIG. 7-27

Light polarizer

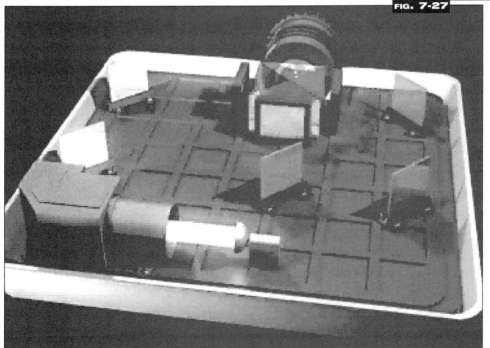

COURTESY: KAYYE CONSULTING

As light would leave the polarizer, it would be reflected through a series of dichroic mirrors to separate the white light into three distinct wavelengths (colors). Dichroic mirrors operate by allowing a certain wavelength of light to pass through, while reflecting all other wavelengths. Through use of these mirrors in series, light is broken down into red, green and blue components.

Once the light is broken into three wavelengths, it is passed through monochromatic LCD panels, each of which is addressed with the appropriate video information for that respective color. Once the remaining light passes through the panels, it is recombined using another series of dichroic mirrors or a combining prism, then sent out through the lens to the projection screen.

Dichroic mirrors system　　**FIG. 7-28**

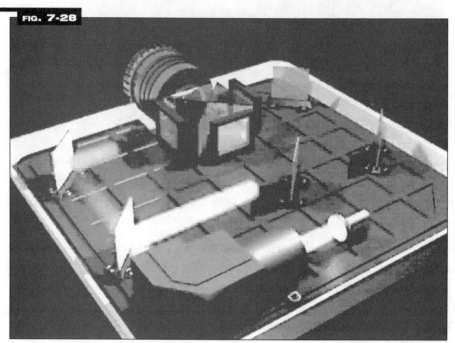

COURTESY: KAYYE CONSULTING

Although this system is very effective, there are some drawbacks, specifically with the amount of light that can pass through the transmissive system. Much of the available light is lost in the transmission process, so intense light is required to create a minimal amount of illumination. Too much light will cause the dichroic components or LCD panels to degrade due to heat damage.

Combining prism　　**FIG. 7-29**

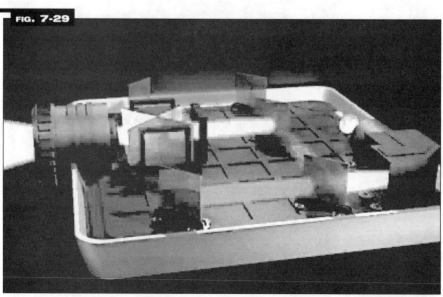

COURTESY: KAYYE CONSULTING

Great strides have been made to improve the efficiency of an LCD system in its ability to pass light. Outside of improvements to the polarization process, the next greatest development came with the implementation of micro-lens array. Traditionally, light that impacted the LCD panel would either pass through the polarizing film on the leading edge of each pixel, or impact the space between pixels. If light impacted the space between the pixels, it would be reflected and eventually lost in the transmission process. Through the incorporation of micro-miniature lenses overlapping each pixel, light that normally would impact between pixels would be re-directed into an adjacent pixel, thus being recaptured into the transmission process. This provided an increase in available light of approximately 30 percent compared with an equivalent non-micro lens array LCD panel.

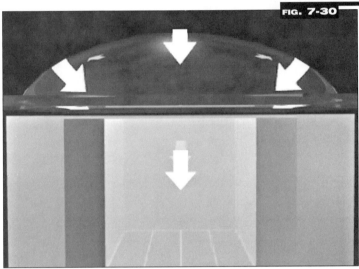

FIG. 7-30

Micro-lens array

COURTESY: KAYYE CONSULTING

The disadvantages of an LCD projector

There are a couple of additional inherent drawbacks to LCD technology. First, LCD panels are not perfect at blocking light within the pixel. When polarized light is not allowed to twist, a certain amount of light is "leaked" through the pixel, creating unwanted light on the projection screen. This light can be substantial in some LCD projectors, creating an artificially high black level in the projection system.

The second inherent drawback to this technology is imperfection in the manufacturing of the LCD panels. Imperfections can result in slight variations in panel density, which can cause greater efficiency in one part of the panel than another. This is perceived on the projection screen as a lack of uniformity.

Despite these drawbacks, LCD technology continues to dominate the conference room marketplace as the technology of choice because of its balance in price and performance. LCD technologies have been implemented in projectors ranging from slightly more than three pounds to large venue projectors weighing hundreds of pounds and producing several thousand lumens of light output.

DLP™ Technology

FIG. 7-31

DLP® DIGITAL LIGHT PROCESSING

A Texas Instruments Technology

COURTESY: TEXAS INSTRUMENTS

Digital light processing (DLP™) technology has played a substantial role in defining the future of projection technology. This technology has pushed the envelope of what is possible with truly mobile projection solutions. At one time, mobile projectors weighing 15 pounds were considered acceptable. Now projection systems weighing six pounds are considered too heavy by some. This technology has been implemented in a variety of configurations, to provide projection systems from the most portable—weighing less than two pounds—to cinema projectors capable of producing more than 15,000 ANSI lumens.

Based on a technology concept developed by RCA in the late 1960s and perfected by Texas Instruments (TI) through the late 1980s, DLP™ uses a reflective image generation device known as the DMD™, or digital micromirror device.

DMD™ chips are manufactured exclusively by Texas Instruments and licensed to projector manufacturers for integration into their projection systems. In the early days of DLP™ projection systems, TI licensed the entire optical assembly, but now projector manufacturers apply their expertise with the technology to create their own optics, and simply license the chip technology from TI.

Unlike an LCD, which is a transmissive system in which light passes through the imaging device to create an image, DLP™ uses a reflective imaging device, whereby light is reflected off an array of pixels to create the image. DLP™ uses two primary implementations: single-chip and three-chip. Although these implementations use the same DMD™ configuration, they differ in the process by which they create color.

In a DLP™ system, the DMD™ is based on a microelectromechanical (MEMS) system that combines a miniaturized mechanical system with microelectronics to drive the movement of an array of micromirrors. Each mirror represents a single picture element in the projected image, and is approximately 16 microns square. The gap between mirrors is less than 1 micron. Each mirror in the array is fabricated over a CMOS (Complimentary Metallic-Oxide Semiconductor) cell, which provides the bias voltage necessary to position the mirror properly. Each mirror is connected to the cell through a yoke, and is allowed to move freely on a series of two torsion hinges. These hinges allow the mirror to move to a range of +10 or ‾10 degrees from its on-axis state in a rotational manner, in relationship to the projector lens system. When the mirrors are on axis with the projection lens, light from the illumination source misses the projection lens; light is allowed to pass through the lens only when the mirror is in the +10 degree state. The state of the SRAM (Static Random Access Memory) cell determines which mirror rotation angle is selected. By applying a bias voltage to one state or another, the mirror position can be switched quickly on its hinge from +10 to ‾10 degrees.

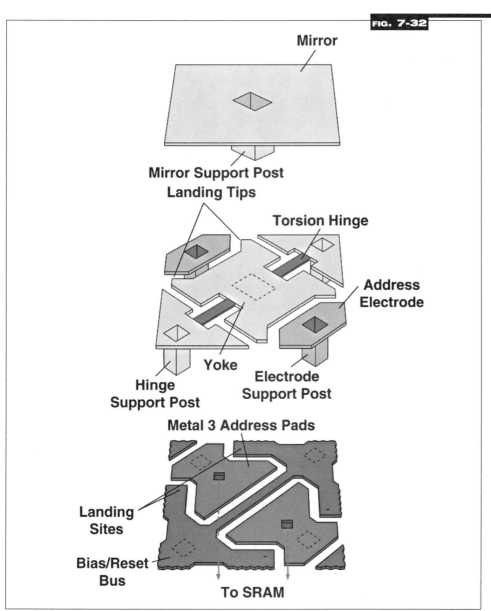

FIG. 7-32

Cutaway of DMD™ chip showing all operating components

Mirror

Mirror Support Post
Landing Tips

Torsion Hinge

Address Electrode

Yoke

Hinge Support Post

Electrode Support Post

Metal 3 Address Pads

Landing Sites

Bias/Reset Bus

To SRAM

COURTESY: TEXAS INSTRUMENTS

The DMD™ accepts electrical "words" representing gray levels of brightness at its input, and puts out optical words. The light modulation or switching technique is called binary pulsewidth modulation. This is different from the technique used in LCD projection, where varying amounts of light are allowed to pass through the pixel to create grayscale images. In a DMD™, by varying the amount of time that light is allowed to reflect off the pixel within a specific time field, any of 256 shades of gray can be created. With a full 20 degrees of separation between the pixel "on" state, where light is reflected into the lens, and the "off" state, where light is reflected away from the lens, excellent contrast can be maintained.

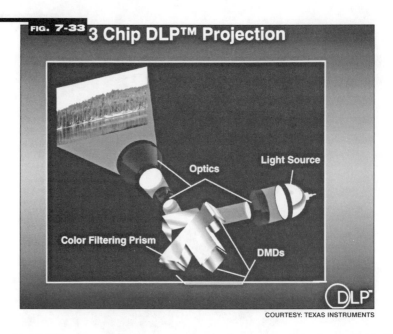

FIG. 7-33 **3 Chip DLP™ Projection**

COURTESY: TEXAS INSTRUMENTS

In a single-chip DLP™ system, light leaves the illumination source (usually a metal halide lamp assembly) and is focused through a condenser lens onto a spinning wheel. This wheel is divided into color segments, which alter the wavelength of light that is presented to the DMD™ chip. When the wheel rotates quickly, the human eye cannot recognize the separate, individual wavelengths, and perceives the sum of all wavelengths.

Color wheel assembly

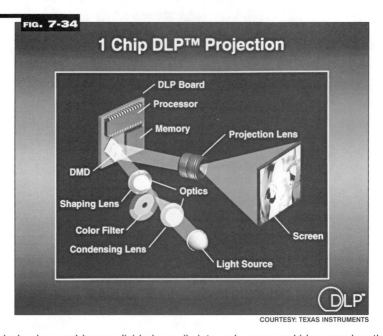

FIG. 7-34

1 Chip DLP™ Projection

COURTESY: TEXAS INSTRUMENTS

The original wheel assembly was divided equally into red, green and blue wavelength segments, but Texas Instruments and projector manufacturers have continued to enhance the colorimetry of the projection system by varying the size and configuration of the color wavelength segments. For instance, introducing a white segment into the wheel produces a contrast boost in the projection system. Doubling the number of segments and dividing the segments in half produces greater perception of color saturation.

Newer wheel designs incorporate a sequential color recapture approach in which the individual wavelengths are transitioned gradually from one to another, as opposed to segmented transitions. This reduces the perception of color "flicker" within the image. The synchronized color information slowly transitions to the DMD™ chip, as well.

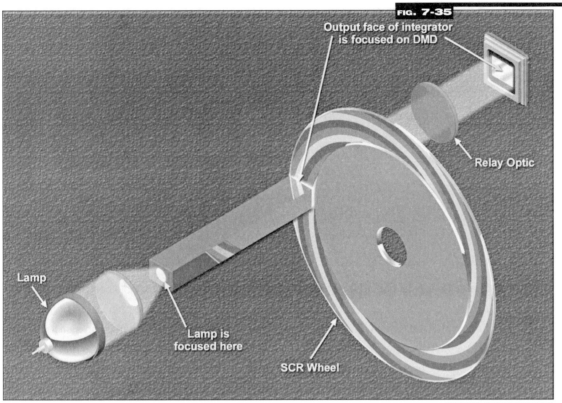

FIG. 7-35

SCR color
wheel
assembly

COURTESY: TEXAS INSTRUMENTS

Once light leaves the wheel assembly, it is focused through a secondary lens that evenly distributes it over the entire surface area of the DMD™ chip. Depending on the state of each mirror
in the DMD™ array, light is reflected through the lens assembly or into light-absorbing material
within the projection system. Directing red picture information to the DMD™ chip when the red
segment of the color wheel interrupts the light path, green picture information with green light
and blue picture information with blue light creates the perception of color.

As the need for higher resolution increases, DMD™ chips are made simply with larger aper-
tures, so that the actual size of each mirror or pixel remains relatively constant. This represents
a significant advantage in the implementation of reflective technology. As the resolution
increases, more light can pass through the optical system, creating a brighter image on the
projection screen. The opposite is true for transmissive technologies, such as LCD. With
greater resolution, the density of pixels is greater, which allows less light to pass through the
array; the result is less overall efficiency and a comparatively dimmer image.

Comparison of different resolution DMD™ chips

COURTESY: TEXAS INSTRUMENTS

The entire optical path of a single chip DLP™ system is relatively simple compared with the complex dichroics involved in LCD projection. This allows the single chip DLP™ projector to be miniaturized for use in the most portable of applications, while maintaining sufficient contrast and colorimetery for video and computer images. The largest differences between DLP™ and LCD technology are in the appearance of the information on-screen. LCD projection has a clearly defined matrix of pixels, due to the relatively large gap between adjacent pixels. This results in clearly defined pixels. By contrast, the very small gap between adjacent pixels in DLP™ projection yields a very smooth, film-like image. Because of this difference, many consider LCD projection most suitable for computer graphics display, and DLP™ most suitable for video display.

Comparison of DLP™ (right) and LCD (left)

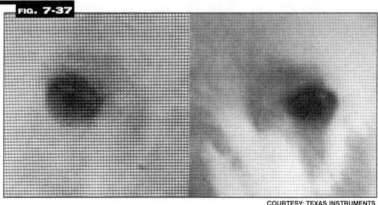

COURTESY: TEXAS INSTRUMENTS

Single-chip DLP™ is optimized for use in mobile projection systems and self-enclosed rear screen projection systems. It has had the most success in the mobile business market, and has found new success in the consumer market with both portable systems and rear projection television systems.

Advantages of a three-chip DLP™ projector

One of the important advantages of DLP™ technology is its resistance to intense heat generated by the illumination source. This allows for projection systems with more than 15,000 ANSI lumens, which is equivalent to the brightest film projectors used in movie theaters.

The alternate method of creating color using DLP™ projection systems is through a linear color creation process similar to LCD projection. This method does not employ a color wheel assembly; that increases the overall efficiency of the projection system and yields the most accurate color reproduction.

FIG. 7-38

Polarizing beam splitter

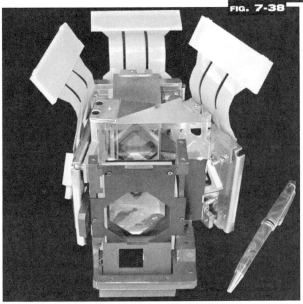

COURTESY: TEXAS INSTRUMENTS

An array of three DMD™ chips is illuminated with an intense illumination source. The light is split into the three primary colors through a polarizing beam splitter, which, like dichroic mirrors, divides the color spectrum into red, green and blue light. The same polarizing beam splitter also acts to recombine the light once it impacts and reflects off the three individual DMD™ chips. When the recombined light leaves the polarizing beam splitter, it is focused through the lens assembly and onto the projection screen. As with single chip DLP™, when a pixel is intended to be black, light is reflected away from the optical assembly within the projector.

FIG. 7-39

Three-chip DLP™ projector

COURTESY: BARCO PROJECTION SYSTEMS

The significant advantage of this implementation is the extremely high contrast that results. Since there is very little filtering of light, a majority of the light is made available to the projection process; this makes the system extremely efficient. Based on the illumination source used, three-chip DLP™ projection systems can be optimized for high-contrast environments; large venues, such as auditoriums; and cinema applications, as the digital replacement for film projectors.

Disadvantages of a three-chip DLP™ projector

The drawback of this technology is that it cannot be miniaturized to the same degree as its counterpart, single-chip DLP™. The sheer size of the optical assembly and the space required to dissipate the heat generated from the illumination source makes this impossible. Thus it is targeted for applications where the size of the projector is not an issue.

One of the most interesting applications is that of digital cinema, or film projector replacement. The drawbacks in film projection are numerous, but the most significant have to do with distribution of media to the theaters and the derogation of film after high use. Distribution of film is a costly endeavor, as the heavy film canisters must be shipped simultaneously to each theater where a specific release is supposed to play. This process is inefficient and costly, and introduces the possibility of theft, loss or delayed releases. Film has a tendency to degrade due to dust accumulation as it is fed multiple times through the film projector. The degradation results in noise in the film. The intense light used in film projectors also has a tendency to cause film to fade, resulting in poor contrast.

Christie digital cinema projector   **FIG. 7-40**

COURTESY: CHRISTIE DIGITAL SYSTEMS

Digital cinema provides a possible solution to these issues and others surrounding the use of film in theaters. By transmitting the content to the theaters digitally, movie creators can control when the content reaches the theater, and even revoke or make changes to the content after the movie has been released. There also is no degradation of the image after multiple uses; the movie remains as fresh as the first time it is run in the theater.

The key to this application is effective use of a high performance digital projection system, such as three-chip DLP™. Projection systems have been optimized to fit the exact footprint of film projectors used in today's theaters. Many also take advantage of the illumination source already used with the film projectors, simply employing an "attachment" to the lamp housing to replace the film projector with a DLP™ projector. The approach minimizes the cost of upgrading the system, and the complexities of installing large lamp housings with significant electrical, space and heat dissipation requirements.

The past and future: alternative reflective technologies

With LCD and DLP™ technologies holding a firm grasp on the vast majority of the market, it is important, even with all of the advancements in their respective technologies, that alternatives remain under continuous development. Most of the leading alternatives use some method of reflective technology, which has proven to have significant potential in extremely high light output environments. The leading alternative contender is a technology called LCOS (liquid crystal on silicon). This is actually a grouping of various technologies, all of which employ a similar implementation. Prior to addressing LCOS, it is important to understand a technology which led to LCOS innovation.

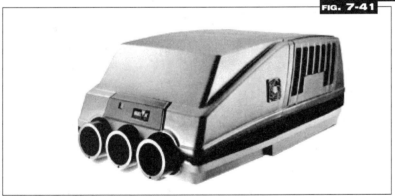

FIG. 7-41

Hughes-JVC 300 series ILA projector

COURTESY: JVC CORPORATION

In the 1980s Hughes developed a technology that was used in high light output applications, primarily for military use. At its inception, this projection technology was capable of producing only monochrome (black and white) images. In the late 1980s, Hughes began looking for a partner to launch a commercialized version of this technology. It found that commercial partner in Victor Company of Japan (JVC). Together the two companies launched ILA (image light amplifier) technology.

ILA technology relied on a hybrid approach of two different imaging technologies, CRT and LCD. The ILA approach was to use the benefit of each of these technologies to create the ultimate display. By using CRT's image-generating capabilities and a lamp technology to provide the illumination, a relatively bright image with film-like images was possible.

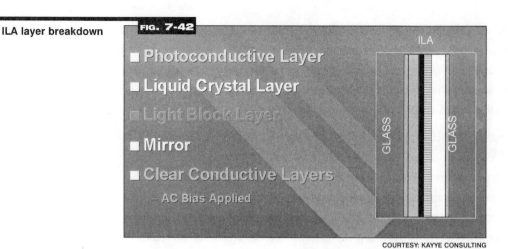

FIG. 7-42

■ Photoconductive Layer

■ Liquid Crystal Layer

■ Light Block Layer

■ Mirror

■ Clear Conductive Layers
— AC Bias Applied

COURTESY: KAYYE CONSULTING

The procedure for creating an image was relatively complex. The CRT used in an ILA projector was relatively small, unlike those used in CRT projectors. The CRT also was coated with an infrared phosphor, as opposed to a red, green or blue phosphor in CRT projectors. The CRT was coupled to the ILA, a proprietary device patented by Hughes. The ILA was organized into multiple layers, the primary ones being a photoconductive layer, a light block layer, a reflective layer and the liquid crystal layer.

The LCD technology used in ILA projection systems was somewhat different from what is in today's LCD projectors; it used a layer of liquid crystal sandwiched between two layers of glass, and did not have a matrix array of rows and columns of pixels.

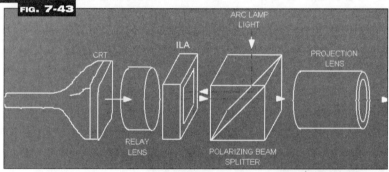

FIG. 7-43

COURTESY: KAYYE CONSULTING

In monochrome ILA operation, an infrared image would be created on the face of the CRT. That infrared image had relatively low light output, and none of the light left the projector. Instead, the infrared light was received by the photoconductive layer of the ILA. This layer would interpret the image electronically, and then transpose it into the liquid crystal layer. When they were stimulated, the liquid crystals would organize in such a manner as to represent the image created by the CRT.

Unlike today's LCD projectors, which rely on light passing through the LCD panel to create an image, the light from the lamp would enter the liquid crystal from the front, pass through the liquid crystal layer, reflect off the reflective layer, and then pass back through the liquid crystal layer. As it passed through the liquid crystal layer, the polarized light would "pick up" the image that had been transposed into the liquid crystal and then passed out through a lens. Light would never pass beyond the reflective layer because of the light block sandwiched in the middle. By using an intense lamp source, very bright images were possible with this technology.

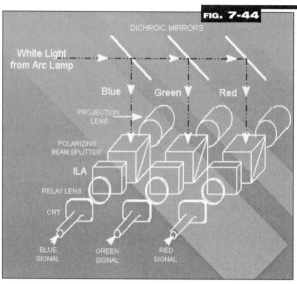

COURTESY: KAYYE CONSULTING

Hughes-JVC created color versions of this technology by using three CRTs and ILAs in a single projector, along with a single lamp light source. Through use of specialized polarizing beam splitters, the light was divided into the three primary wavelengths of red, green and blue, each of which would pass into the ILA. (All three CRTs would create the same infrared light to drive the ILAs.)

The advantages of this technology were obvious. High-contrast images were possible with the image quality of a scanning-based imaging system. Since the imaging system was CRT, variable resolutions were possible, without the side-effects of a matrix-based system. By simply changing the size of the illumination source, brighter projectors could be created.

The drawbacks of this technology, though, led to the demise of this reflective technology. Since it was CRT-based, it was susceptible to the same characteristics that affect CRT projectors. ILA projectors were susceptible to burn-in, although not as severe as that with CRT projectors since the illumination of the CRT was minimal. The size of the ILA system was immense, with the combination of three CRTs, three ILAs, a lamp and lamp power supply, along with the weight of three high quality lenses. It was not uncommon for these projectors to weigh more than 300 pounds.

In addition, these systems were very complex to align, because they involved external convergence and creating uniformity in the three ILAs. Hughes-JVC was able to reduce this complexity somewhat with the introduction of an internally converged system that used a single lens. By using a series of internal lenses and combining prisms, all three primary wavelengths of light could be recombined to pass through a single lens assembly. This did little to reduce the mass of the projector, however; they still weighed more than 250 pounds.

Hughes-JVC 200 series ILA projector

COURTESY: JVC CORPORATION

PROJECTION TECHNOLOGIES

The last drawback to these systems was the uniformity of the liquid crystal layer. Since the area of this layer was relatively large (more than 3 inches diagonally), it was extremely difficult to manufacture the liquid crystal layer in equal density throughout the ILA. The result was that, as light passed through the liquid crystal, areas of greater density appeared darker on the projection screen. The solution to this defect in the manufacturing process was an electronic compensation that provided contrast adjustments throughout the image. Known as "shading", it allowed the technician to vary the contrast in a specific area of the screen until the uniformity defects were no longer noticeable. This resulted in a very prolonged setup process, which could occupy as much as eight hours on a single projector.

D-ILA device

FIG. 7-46

COURTESY: JVC CORPORATION

Even though the ILA was overtaken in the market by high light output LCD and the quick emergence of three-chip DLP™, the technology was not forgotten. As Hughes floundered, JVC continued innovation of the ILA concept. JVC became focused on the miniaturization of the entire ILA system. The concept was to use an LCD matrix as the imaging technology, in place of the CRT. Light would never pass through this LCD matrix, though, thus the LCD matrix could be of extremely high resolution (1,365 x 1,024 at inception). Its image would simply be transposed into a liquid crystal layer, in much the same way that the ILA operated. By replacing the CRT with a high resolution LCD, the size of the ILA could also be miniaturized, thus eliminating the shading issues that plagued the ILA. With the "new" ILA, the entire system, including the LCD matrix, was reduced to a device smaller than a postage stamp. That new system became known as D-ILA. By combining three of the D-ILA chips with a light source and the necessary polarizing beam splitters and combining prisms, a high-resolution projector of very small size was possible.

Ultimately Hughes disappeared from the picture and JVC continued with development of D-ILA architecture. Other technology manufacturers noticed JVC's success with a high-resolution LCD technology and created similar implementations. These technologies have become known as LCOS, or liquid crystal on silicon. Not all employ the multilayered approach that JVC undertook, but all use a reflective system combined with a matrix array of LCD pixels to create the image. With more than 20 manufacturers working on the development of LCOS technology, there is great potential for LCOS to play a vital role in the future of projection technology.

Other areas of development have occurred with alternative reflective technologies, including MEMS, or micro-electrical-mechanical systems. This category includes DLP™ technology as well as new, competing reflective micro-mirror technologies. These new developments have improved the resolution-generating device itself, or the illumination source used to provide the light output.

Other MEMS technologies have employed a similar approach to DLP™, in which one or more micro-mirrors are used to represent each pixel within the projection image. In addition to the hinge approach, where the mirror mechanically moves on a hinge, some alternative technologies have employed a "ribbon" approach, where each pixel is composed of multiple ribbon-like structures that can be moved up

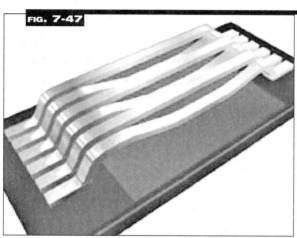

FIG. 7-47

SLM GLV imaging device

COURTESY: SILICON LIGHT MACHINES

or down over a very small distance (only a fraction of the wavelength of light) by the control of electrostatic forces. The ribbons are arranged such that each pixel is capable of reflecting either toward a lens assembly or away from it. This allows an array of pixels to vary the level of light reflected off the surface of the chip. The control of light can be analog, where variable amounts of light are reflected off the pixel, or digital, where the amount of time in which light is reflected in a given interval dictates the intensity of the pixel. These systems hold potential for extremely flexible implementations, depending on the application they serve.

The other advancements in technologies come in the form of alternatives to the use of a lamp assembly as an illumination source. One such advancement is the use of lasers to create the intensity that is reflected off a MEMS or LCOS device. By employing an array of monochromatic red, blue and green lasers specifically designed and optimized for projection systems, the need for beam splitters and complex optics can be reduced significantly. As small, tunable solid-state lasers continued to advance, true color wavelength accuracy and saturation unachievable using any "white light" source becomes possible. In addition, solid-state lasers are reliable and produce excellent efficiencies in power consumption per lumen of light output.

Each of the three lasers produces highly coherent light. The light travels from projector to screen with very little divergence compared with ordinary white light from a lamp, which diverges greatly, even with collimating optics and parabolic reflectors. This capability of laser light results in a much greater depth of field, so that images can be projected onto irregular (curved) surfaces without special optics, and remain in focus.

Another advantage of laser technology is that the intensity of the pixel can be controlled through changes in the intensity of the laser at the point where it impacts the pixel. This method of scanning an image across the array yields a very high contrast image in which pixels that are intended to be dark actually are created by the absence of light from the laser at the point of impact within the scanning process. The result is black levels similar to those found in CRT projection systems.

By employing this scanning technique in combination with a MEMS device that possesses a wide range of reflective capabilities, a single column of pixels can be used to create an entire image. Each row within the projected image is represented by a single pixel, and on diffraction within the MEMS device creates the columns of pixels. As the laser illuminates the reflective picture element, that element shifts its angle and modulates the laser light to create the next horizontal pixel. When the next row in the image is created, the next pixel in the vertical array takes over. Thus significantly fewer pixels are necessary within the imaging device. An HDTV display within 1,920x1,080 resolution requires a vertical column of 1,080 pixels, while traditional lamp systems with a fixed array of pixels require 1,920x1,080 or 2,073,600 pixels.

SLM GLC imaging process

FIG. 7-48

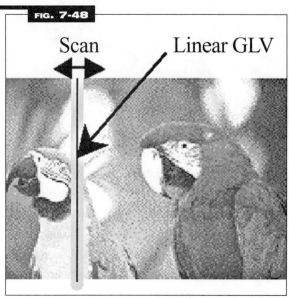

COURTESY: SILICON LIGHT MACHINES

8 THE AUDIO IN

AUDIOVISUAL

edited by **STEVE THORBURN, PE, CTS-D, CTS-I**

Steven J. Thorburn, PE, CTS-D, CTS-I, is the
co-founder of Thorburn Associates, Inc.,
a full service acoustical and audiovisual
design and engineering firm with offices in
the Los Angeles, San Francisco and
Raleigh-Durham, N.C., areas.
He specializes in acoustics, audiovisual
design, and project management
of presentation systems and facilities.
He can be reached at SJT@TA-Inc.com.

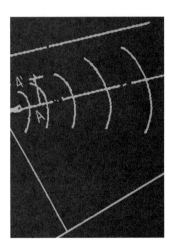

There is perhaps no other segment of audiovisual technology that benefits from as much prerequisite knowledge and experience as the design of audio systems. Yet there seems to be a tendency for the designer to skirt the acoustical calculations and take the audio system for granted. The choice of loudspeaker often is based on the designer's having found the perfect speaker: compact, medium cost, and rated by some magazine as the surround sound speaker of the month. Its location is more a matter of where it will fit rather than where it belongs. Well-recognized rules-of-thumb often are ignored completely. Confusion exists in differentiating among PA (public address) systems, voice reinforcement systems, multimedia sound systems and concert/theater sound systems. Audio processing equipment is chosen on the basis of budget or name recognition, and not necessarily on quality.

What is the reason for this apparent gap in audio system design proficiency? Most likely it stems from the fact that audio system engineering is not easy to understand. It is not a compact, readily learned bit of technology. Its basics are learned on a professional engineering level, augmented by years of practical experience. Its technical roots reach into physics, acoustics, psycho-acoustics, speech, mathematics, electronics and even architecture.

With the spread of technology today, it is difficult to draw lines of demarcation in professional design areas. In many cases the sound system specialist, who in past years was exactly that, today is a complete audio-visual-network-system contractor. Typically the specialist started out in the sound business, selling, renting, installing and servicing all kinds of audio equipment, from that used in church fairs and high school auditoriums to the large systems needed for political rallies and football stadiums. During those years, the term *sound system* was not linked with audiovisual presentation, but it wasn't long before the sound-system contractor's domain expanded to include both sound and visuals.

Now history is repeating itself. Just as the overlapping activities of sound-system contractors and their visual system counterparts led to the audiovisual contracting business, networking and control system components have come together to form the new business of systems contracting, or system integration.

Finally, there are acoustic consultants, audiovisual consultants and communications facilities consultants. Such consultants, by the very nature of their profession, are not installation contractors or equipment suppliers. They design systems, specify their components, interconnections and operation, and prepare working drawings for systems. But it is the installation contractors who take responsibility for supplying and installing a successful system. On their knowledge and expertise depends the success of the final system.

The more one studies the techniques of audio system engineering, the clearer it becomes that much of the subject matter is tied to the field of acoustics. Sooner or later the audio-system designer must gain a working knowledge of room acoustics, including: reverberation time, absorption coefficients, sound attenuation, sound pressure level, critical distance and a host of other pertinent factors that are necessary to the design of an optimum sound system for a given space.

It seems logical that an acoustical consultant, who has collaborated with the architect to design the given space, would be eminently qualified to design the sound system for that space. And such is often the case. In certain parts of the country, it is common practice for acoustical consultants to design the sound system as an integral part of their work. This is true especially for large projects such as music halls, theaters and coliseums. The practice sometimes carries over into smaller projects, such as corporate auditoriums and lecture halls, even though these spaces are more audiovisually oriented.

So we see that there are all levels of knowledge represented by those who design and install sound systems for audiovisual installations. Obviously this book cannot cover all the technical prerequisites of such a wide spectrum of audio technology, for one reader may need a review of decibels, and another reader may be interested in "the attenuation of sound in reverberant space." As stated in the preface, this is a basic text, dealing with fundamental concepts and procedures. Our discussion in this section therefore will be confined to some vital and basic concepts concerning sound pressure, sound power and sound intensity, proceeding to a discussion of the decibel and its use in audio calculations. The remainder of the section will show how these concepts form the basis of audiovisual system design, and permit us to investigate the behavior of sound in enclosed areas. Space does not allow the usual descriptive discussion of loudspeakers, microphones, amplifiers and other audio components. The available literature amply covers this material. Rather, we will stress the basic design calculations. The section concludes with typical audio system design examples involving loudspeakers, microphones, sound levels and amplifier power requirements.

The concept of sound pressure: the pascal, or newton per square meter

Sound, as depicted in Figure 8-1, is the result of a wave motion created by some vibrating source, transmitted through some medium (air in our case), and received by some receptor (the ear) that acts as a transducer to assist the brain in interpreting the wave motion pressure as sound.

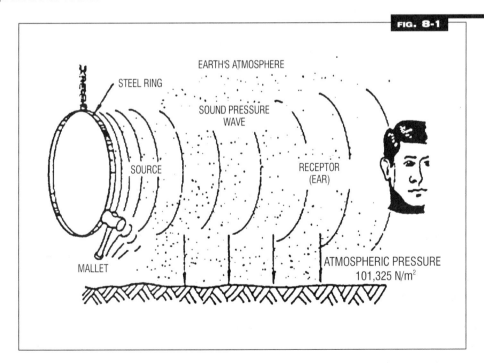

FIG. 8-1

Sound waves striking the human ear

Air is an elastic medium and is capable of successive compression and expansion, causing extremely minute changes in the earth's static ambient air pressure in the path of a propagating sound wave. Readers who have not studied physics may be surprised to learn that the weight of all the air above the surface of the earth is considerable, amounting to 14.7 pounds pressing down on every square inch of surface at sea level.

The most practical display of this fact is a crude demonstration wherein a pint of water is poured into a thin metal 5-gallon container. The container is left uncapped while heat is applied, and the water is boiled until the entire container is full of steam, thus expelling all the air within. The container is now tightly capped, and the heat source removed. As the container cools, the steam inside condenses, creating a vacuum and leaving little or no air pressure inside to resist the external force of the earth's atmosphere. Result: The container is crushed as though a truck had run over it.

We can see why the human body, unlike the container, does not collapse under the weight of the atmosphere: We do not have a vacuum inside us. The atmospheric pressure is within us and surrounds us; consequently we are not aware of this pressure at sea level. In the absence of any sound waves (air pressure fluctuations), our ears would not perform their hearing function, because the air pressure on each side of the eardrum would be equalized. Any sound wave pressure encountered by the outer ear and eardrum is superimposed on the steady-state atmospheric pressure on our middle ear, which then transmits the pressure fluctuations to our inner ear. The inner ear is the section where the pressure change is passed to the nerve endings in our ear. This is the auditory mechanism whereby our ear and brain produce the sensation of sound.

Inner ear auditory mechanism

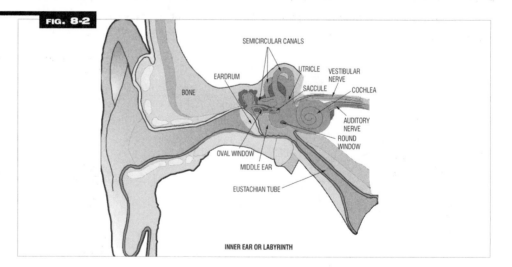

FIG. 8-2

SEMICIRCULAR CANALS
UTRICLE
VESTIBULAR NERVE
EARDRUM
SACCULE
COCHLEA
BONE
AUDITORY NERVE
ROUND WINDOW
OVAL WINDOW
MIDDLE EAR
EUSTACHIAN TUBE
INNER EAR OR LABYRINTH

The most remarkable thing about the function of the human ear is the unbelievable range of sound pressures over which it operates from the minutest pressure (such as the sound of fluttering insect wings) to the pressure propagated by the deafening roar of a jet engine at take-off. This range spans a sound pressure ratio of 10 million to one.

A suitable unit of pressure measurement would have to be, by definition, some unit of force acting on a unit area, such as the familiar pounds per square inch. However, the pressures we are talking about are so small that we need a much smaller unit. The metric system offers smaller units, is preferred throughout the scientific world and is known as SI, from "Systeme International d'Unites." This system is based on the meter, kilogram, second, ampere, Kelvin and candela units for measuring the basic quantities of length, mass, time, electric current, thermodynamic temperature and luminous intensity. American readers already are faced with enough confusion in converting their thinking from the familiar English system of measurement to the metric system, without now having to think in terms of the more recent SI system. Consequently this text will use the more familiar MKS (meter, kilogram, second) metric system. In any event, the starting place will be the pressure of the atmosphere at sea level and 68° F, or 20° C, as this is standard the world over. By definition 1 earth atmosphere is 101,325 N/m^2 (Newton per square meter). One pascal equals one newton per square meter.

This is rounded off to 100,000, or 1×10^5 N/m^2, using scientific notation (1×10^5, = 1 + five zeros). The human ear is so sensitive that it can detect sound wave pressures as low as 2×10^{-5} N/m^2. This tiny pressure represents the threshold of hearing, and has become the standard sound pressure level against which all louder sounds are measured.

The concept of sound power, or acoustic work

In all forms of energy transfer, work is done. It is not until work is accomplished that energy is useful. The doing of work always implies that a certain amount of energy is expended in a certain time. We must remember that energy and work, as well as any other quantities, can be expressed in more ways than one, as long as the expressions yield the same result. The metric system uses watts to measure all kinds of work, not just electrical power. By definition,

1 watt = 1 Newton-meter/second

As an exercise, let us see how many watts are equivalent to 1 horsepower (see Figure 8-3).

1 hp = 550 ft-lb/second (English system)

Converting to the metric system,

1 ft = .3046 meters (m)

1 lb = 4.448 Newtons

1 hp = (550 ft-lb/s) x (.3048 m/ft) x (4.448 N/lb)=745.66 N-m/s

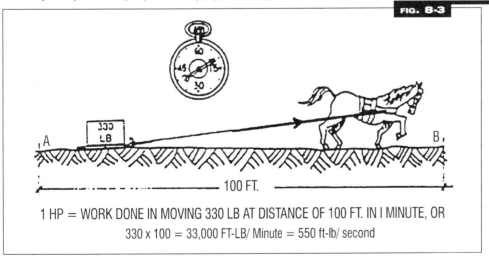

FIG. 8-3   **Calculation of 1 horsepower**

1 HP = WORK DONE IN MOVING 330 LB AT DISTANCE OF 100 FT. IN I MINUTE, OR
330 x 100 = 33,000 FT-LB/ Minute = 550 ft-lb/ second

The concept of sound intensity: the watts/meter²

We have mentioned watts as a measure of power, or total work done per second. But now w want to see how intense that work is, or how much of it is performed over a specific area, su as 1 square meter. Hence the expression watts/meter². The more work done over a specific area, the more intense the sound will be. The intensity of sound may be defined as the soun energy per second passing through a unit area.

If there were a point source of sound, pressure waves would radiate spherically about the source, permeating the space around it evenly in all directions. Figure 8-4 shows how the energy flows radially outward from the source. But to measure how much energy is flowing i given time and in a certain location, we need to examine a small volumetric section of an ima nary spherical shell. We can then see how much energy is flowing through this volume in 1 second. The reason we talk about a volume is that we have dyne-centimeters per square cer timeter, and distance times area equals volume.

Actually we are talking about the amount of acoustic energy that is required to displace a un volume of air (1m³) in 1 second, by virtue of the sound pressure exerted by the sound wave. Sound intensity is the measure of this acoustic energy. Its symbol is "I", and its units are watts/meter². The last remaining hurdle is to understand how the intensity, I, is evaluated. Hei the equation:

$$\text{Sound intensity} = I = \frac{p^2}{\rho c^1}$$

Stated in words, this says that intensity equals the square of the sound pressure divided by t product of the air density and the velocity of sound. It is traditional to use the Greek letter rhc "ρ" for air density, and also "C" for the velocity of sound. The symbol "p" represents the sou pressure. As for units,

I = watts/m²
p = sound pressure in kg/m²
ρ = standard air density = 1.17959 kg/m², and
c = velocity of sound at sea level = 344.75 m/sec

But why is p squared, and why does ρc enter the equation?

While it is beyond the scope of this brief treatment to examine the derivation of the intensity equation, we can note that it is the result of applying the principles of force, mass, acceleratic and work to air particles in a wave motion. The form of the equation reminds us of the well-known electrical expression for power, wherein

$$P = \frac{E^2}{R}$$

The E^2 is voltage (pressure) squared, and the R is electrical resistance (impedance). In the sound intensity equation, p^2 is likewise the acoustic pressure squared, and the term ρc is like wise called the acoustic resistance of air (impedance), or the resistance the sound pressure wave must overcome in propagating itself in air at the speed of sound.

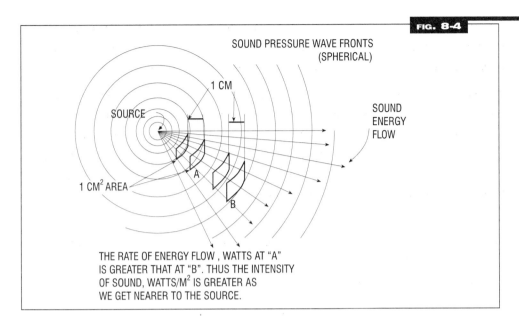

FIG. 8-4

Sound pressure is greater
nearer the source

SOUND PRESSURE WAVE FRONTS
(SPHERICAL)

1 CM

SOURCE

SOUND
ENERGY
FLOW

1 CM² AREA

A

B

THE RATE OF ENERGY FLOW , WATTS AT "A"
IS GREATER THAT AT "B". THUS THE INTENSITY
OF SOUND, WATTS/M² IS GREATER AS
WE GET NEARER TO THE SOURCE.

The acoustic impedance of air is, in numbers,

rc = density of air x velocity of sound

$= 1.179659 \text{ kg/m}^3 \times 344.754 \text{ m/s}$

$= 406.692 \text{ N - s/m}^3$ or 407 Rayls

This number is a constant at sea level and 20˚C, and is also referred to as 42 acoustic ohms.

We have just examined three very important concepts: sound pressure, sound power and sound intensity. It will be some time before the reader who is unfamiliar with these concepts can feel comfortable with them. At this point, it would be advantageous to pause and spend a little time on the practical use of these quantities. This is more easily done, however, after reviewing the important unit of measurement used so frequently in audio work: the decibel.

A measuring scale is needed: the decibel

Now that we have defined sound pressure, sound power and sound intensity, and have become familiar with the units in which they are expressed, we will consider the way in which our sense of hearing responds to these stimuli. The measurement of sound is aimed at approximating the reaction of the ear to sound pressure waves of varying intensities. Consequently the ratio of two sound intensities, I_2 and I_1, is expressed logarithmically, which is the way the ear evaluates different levels of sound. The unit that expresses this logarithmic ratio is the bel, named after Alexander Graham Bell.

So we have

$$\text{bels} = \log_{10} \frac{I_2}{I_1}$$

It should be noted here that the human response to stimulation of our senses closely follows a logarithmic curve. This means simply that the response is approximately proportional to the logarithm of the stimulus; it is not directly proportional to the stimulus. In other words, the relationship between cause and effect is not linear, but logarithmic. Thus, a light source that is emitting twice as many light units as another, by actual measurement, does not look twice as bright to the eye. It appears to be only about 1/3 brighter (the log of 2 is 0.301). What a difficult thing to evaluate! It is difficult because it involves human reaction, which does not have numbers on it, and because there are so many different reactions possible, depending on the color temperature of the light, the color of the surround, the age of the observer and so on.

We react to sound in a similar way. When is one sound twice as loud as another? Could we identify a sound three times as loud as another? How many times louder than a sewing machine is a tractor motor? The ear is affected by pitch (frequency), loudness (amplitude) and intensity, as well as by other physical and psychological factors. So we can appreciate that measuring human response is a very subjective thing. The best we can do is accept the findings of researchers who have been concerned with the problem for the best part of the last century.

Getting back to the bel, a smaller unit was needed to be more compatible with the smallest change in intensity to which the ear can respond. Therefore a tenth of a bel was employed and called the decibel, abbreviated dB. Referring to our equation for the bel, we can now write

$$dB = 10 \log_{10} \frac{I_2}{I_1}$$

We multiply the right-hand side by 10 because, if dB is a smaller unit, more decibels are required to equal the given intensity change. The decibel tells not how much but how many times one quantity exceeds another. It is strictly a ratio, not an absolute quantity. The decibel is therefore dimensionless.

It may be used, for example, to express sound pressure ratios, for we can substitute the value of I (intensity), found earlier, in the dB expression to get

$$dB = 10 \log_{10} \frac{\dfrac{p_2^2}{\rho c}}{\dfrac{p_1^2}{\rho c}} \quad 10 \log_{10} \left(\frac{p_2}{p_1}\right)^2$$

$$= 20 \log_{10} \frac{p_2}{p_1}$$

Recall that in logarithmic manipulations the exponent 2 is brought down and multiplied by the coefficient of the log term, producing the multiplier of 20. We see that when power-like quantities such as sound intensities, sound power, audio power amplifiers and loudspeaker power ratings are compared, we use the 10 multiplier, and when ratios of pressure-like quantities such as sound pressure level and voltages are involved, the multiplier becomes 20. The common logarithm always is used in these kinds of calculations, and for simplicity we will omit the base 10 subscript in any following logarithmic terms.

The decibel scale would have no meaning if it did not have a zero starting place. Remember, the decibel compares two quantities. In the case of sound pressures, for example, when we are dealing with the sound pressure level of a single sound, a second sound pressure actually is taken automatically as the least audible sound that the ear can hear. The given decibel value is then telling us that the given sound has a sound pressure level that many times as great as the threshold of sound. We learned earlier that the threshold of sound is 0.00002 (2×10^{-5}) N/m^2 or 20 micropascals.

dB-SPL

If we say that the sound pressure level (hereafter referred to as SPL) of a nearby jet engine at take-off is 140 dB at 50', we mean that the SPL of the engine sound is 140 times greater than the SPL of a sound that the ear can just hear. Accordingly, to avoid confusion we must always quote the reference level when dealing with sound pressure levels in decibels. The correct terminology for the given example is 140 dB-SPL re: 2×10^{-5} N/m^2, at 50'. Table 8-1 gives some familiar sound pressure levels, listed in descending order from the loudest sound the ear can tolerate to the faintest sound, or threshold of hearing. This is done conveniently in eight steps, each step ten times the magnitude of the preceding step. Column 3 shows that with the zero of the dB scale at the lowest audible sound pressure, all other values are greater, and are plus quantities. If we had selected some other value for the zero point on the scale, say the sound pressure due to a loud auto horn at 10 feet 2 N/m^2, we would end up with negative values for all lesser sounds, as shown in column 4. This is not as convenient as an all-positive scale.

If we did not use the decibel scale and dealt just with the linear sound pressures, the jet engine sound pressure would be 10 million times as intense as the threshold of sound, $200 \div 0.00002 = 10,000,000$. Certainly the jet engine sound is more intense than a sound we can just hear, but do we judge it to be 10 million times louder? It is obvious that the ear does not hear linearly. Let us use the dB-SPL equation to check the Table 8-1 value of 60 dB-SPL for heavy auto and truck traffic 100' from the highway.

$$\text{dB-SPL} = 20 \log \frac{p_2}{p_1}$$

where

$p_2 = 0.02$ N/m^2

$p_1 = 0.00002$ N/m^2

dB-SPL = 20 log (0.02/0.00002) = 20 log 1000 = 20 x 3

= 60dB-SPL re 0.00002 N/m^2 @ 100 ft.

Whenever we talk about dB sound pressure levels, the symbol dB-SPL must be used, along with the reference level and distance. Sound pressure levels are measured on a sound level meter calibrated to read directly in decibels, referenced to the threshold of sound.

TABLE 8-1 Typical sound pressures and their decibel levels relative to the threshold of sound

Linear Scale of Sound Pressures Newtons per square meter 1	Example 2	dB-SPL re:0.00002 N/m^2 3	dB-SPL re: 2 N/m^2 4
200	Near Jet Engine at Take off (Threshold of Pain)	140	40
20	Hard Rock Band on Stage (Threshold of Feeling)	120	20
2	Loud Auto Horn at 10 feet	100	0
0.2	School Cafeteria with Glazed Cement Block Walls	80	-20
0.02	Heavy Auto & Truck Traffic 100 Feet From Highway	60	-40
0.002	Soft Radio Music in Living Room	40	-60
0.0002	Average Whisper Studio for Sound Pictures	20	-80
0.00002	Threshold of Hearing (young people. 1000 to 4000 Hz)	0	-100

dB-PWL

Sound power should not be confused with sound pressure. Recall that sound power is the capacity for doing work, and is expressed in watts in the metric system. But the work we are talking about is acoustic work. An acoustic device may draw 1,000 watts of electrical energy from the power line to make it operate, but because of the low acoustic efficiency of the audio device, it may generate only 10 watts of acoustic power. This is what is meant by sound power. The measurement of acoustic power is not a simple, direct measurement, like sound pressure; it must be calculated from sound pressure measurements.

Table 8-2 is similar to the sound pressure listing in Table 8-1 and can be used to find the sound power of various sources and to calculate their decibel sound power levels.

TABLE 8-2 Typical sound power outputs and their decibel levels relative to the threshold of sound

Linear Scale of Sound Pressures Newtons per square meter 1	Example 2	dB-PWL re: 10^{-12} Watts 3
(10^5) 100,000	Large Jet Airliner at Take off	170
(10^4) 10,000	Turbo Jet Engine 7000 Lb. Thrust	160
(10^3) 1000	Helicopter at Take off	150
(10^2) 100	4 Engine Prop. Plane at Take off	140
(10^1) 10	Symphony Orchestra Fortissimo	130
(10^0) 1	Pneumatic Chipping Hammer	120
(10^{-1}) 0.1	Automobile on Highway	110
(10^{-2}) 0.01	Ventilating Fan	100
(10^{-3}) 0.001	Loud Shout	90
(10^{-4}) 0.0001	Radio Volume Turned Up	80
(10^{-5}) 0.00001	Conversational Voice	70
(10^{-6}) 0.000001	Low Voice	60
(10^{-9}) 0.000000001	Soft Whisper	30
(10^{-12}) 0.000000000001	Threshold of Hearing	0

Here again, the linear scale represents a ratio of power level over its entire range of 1×10^5 divided by $10^{-12} = 1 \times 10^{17}$ to 1. In decibel notation, this same range of power level is expressed by a range of 170 dB.

This value is found as follows:

$$\text{dB-PWL} = 10 \log \frac{P_2}{P_1}$$

where

$P_2 = 100,000$ watts (from table for jetliner)
$P_1 = 0.000000000001$ watt (threshold of hearing)

$$\text{dB-PWL} = 10 \log \frac{1 \times 10^5}{1 \times 10^{-12}} = 10 \log \left(1 \times 10^{17} \right)$$

$$= 10 \times 17$$
$$= 170 \text{ dB}$$

Recall that the logarithm of a number which can be expressed as 1×10^n, where n is a whole number, is simply n. Whenever we talk about sound power levels, the symbol dB-PWL is used, along with the reference level.

It is often convenient to simplify both the dB-SPL and dB-PWL expressions for use with the standard reference levels.

We can therefore write

$$\text{dB-SPL} = 20 \log \frac{p_2}{0.00002} \quad 20 (\log p_2 - \log 0.00002)$$

$$= 20 \log p_2 - 20(-4.69897)$$

$$= 20 \log p_2 + 94 \text{ re } 0.00002 \text{ N/m}^2$$

In a similar manner,

$$\text{dB-PWL} = 10 \log \frac{P_2}{1 \times 10^{-12}}$$

$$= 10(\log P_2 - \log 1 \times 10^{-12})$$

$$= 10 \log P_2 - 10 (-12)$$

$$= 10 \log P_2 + 120 \text{ re: } 10^{-12} \text{ watts}$$

Working with sound pressure levels outdoors

In audio system design we are interested in sound pressure levels because every AV system has a source of sound, whether it is the unaided human voice, a live orchestra or sound that is transmitted via a loudspeaker system to the listener. Our chief interest, other than sound quality, is to be sure that the sound reaches the ear of the listener with sufficient level to permit effortless hearing.

The way in which sound level decreases as the sound travels from its source is called attenuation. Sound attenuates differently outdoors than indoors. This is because the outdoor environment is a non-reverberant space, while indoors the sound is reflected and absorbed by the interior surfaces, audience and furniture. There are two useful rules that apply when dealing with sound pressure levels and the attenuation of sound outdoors.

Rule 1

If the power input to a sound source is doubled, the SPL at a given distance will be increased by 3 dB. Conversely, if the power input to a sound source is halved, the SPL at a given distance will be decreased by 3 dB. This relationship is apparent from the basic decibel expression for all power-like ratios:

$$\text{dB} = 10 \log \frac{P_2}{P_1}$$

If power P_2 is twice as large as P_1, then $\dfrac{P_2}{P_1} = 2$, and

$$\text{dB} = 10 \log 2 = 10 \times 0.301 = +3 \text{ dB (increase)}$$

If P_2 is $1/2 P_1$, then

$$\text{dB} = 10 \log 0.5 = 10(-0.301) = -3 \text{ dB (decrease)}$$

The minus sign indicates that the sound pressure dropped.

Rule 2

If the distance from the sound source to the measuring point is doubled, the sound pressure decreases by 6 dB, or is 6 dB down (-6dB). The converse is also true. Rule 2 involves the inverse square law, which says that for a given sound power the sound intensity at a given distance, d_1, compared with the intensity at a greater distance, d_2, will vary inversely as the square of the distance. Mathematically we can write this inverse variation as

$$\frac{I_2}{I_1} = \left(\frac{d_1}{d_2}\right)^2$$

but we have already learned that $\dfrac{I_2}{I_1} = \left(\dfrac{p_2}{p_1}\right)^2$; therefore,

from the basic decibel expression for all voltage-like (pressure) ratios, which require the 20 multiplier,

$$dB = 20 \log\left(\frac{p_2}{p_1}\right) = 20 \log\left(\frac{d_1}{d_2}\right) = 20 \log\left(\frac{1}{2}\right) = 20 \log 0.5$$

$$= 20 (-.301) = -6 \text{ dB, or 6 dB down.}$$

A few examples showing the application of what we have learned so far in this section should help the reader feel more comfortable about working with decibels, sound intensities, sound pressure levels, sound power levels and sound attenuation outdoors. Later in this section we will tackle typical problems for indoor spaces, which become much more involved, because sound behaves quite differently in reverberant spaces.

Example 1

The Table 8-1 of typical sound pressures given earlier shows that a loud auto horn at a distance of 10' from a listener creates a sound wave that with a pressure of 2 N/m^2 on the eardrum. Calculate the dB value given in column 3 of the table.

Solution:

$$p_2 = 2 \text{ N/m}^2, \text{ from table}$$

$$p_1 = 0.00002 \text{ N/m}^2, \text{ threshold of sound}$$

$$dB\text{-}SPL = 20 \log\left(\frac{p_2}{p_1}\right) = 20 \log\left(\frac{2}{0.00002}\right)$$

$$= 20 \log (1 \times 10^5)$$

$$= 20 \times 5 = 100$$

We will check this answer by using the simplified equation given in the text:

$$dB\text{-}SPL = 20 \log(p_2) + 94 = 20 \log(2) + 94 = (20 \times 0.301) + 94$$

$$= 6 + 94 = 100$$

Sometimes there is confusion between sound pressure levels and sound power levels, because both are expressed in decibels. This reminds us that the decibel is not a measuring unit of some kind of sound; it does not express a measurement, like pounds/sq inch or miles/hr. It tells us only how many times more, or less, one quantity is compared with another, in decibels. With sound pressure levels, the decibel value compares two sound pressures, measured in N/m^2. The larger one is the given source, and the smaller one is the threshold of hearing, 2×10^{-5} N/m^2.

If we're talking about sound power levels, the decibel value compares two sound power levels measured in watts. The larger value is the sound power of the given source, and the smaller is the sound power output of a source at the threshold of hearing, 1×10^{-12} watt. This is 1.0 with the decimal point moved 12 decimal places to the left, or 0.000000000001 watt.

Example 2

Table 8-2 of typical sound power outputs shows that a ventilating fan produces a sound power of 0.01 watt. Show by calculation that the sound power level agrees with the tabular value of 100 dB-PWL re: 10^{-12} watt.

Solution:

$$P_2 = 0.01 \text{ watt, from table}$$

$$P_1 = 10^{-12} \text{ watt, threshold of sound}$$

$$\text{dB-PWL} = 10 \log\left(\frac{P_2}{P_1}\right) = 10 \log\left(\frac{1 \times 10^{-2}}{1 \times 10^{-12}}\right)$$

$$= 10 \log(1 \times 10^{10})$$

$$= 10 \times 10 = 100$$

If we use the simplified equation in the text,

$$\text{dB-PWL} = 10 \log(1 \times 10^{-2}) + 120 = 10(-2) + 120$$

$$= -20 + 120 = 100$$

Example 3

Figure 8-5 shows a loudspeaker on a pole that is aimed at a point B, distance of 300', measured along the speaker axis. At a point A, 4' from the horn, a sound level meter shows an SPL reading of 128 dB re: 2×10^{-5} N/m^2. Find the sound pressure level at point B, the listener's location. This is a problem in inverse square law attenuation outdoors.

Solution:

Find the attenuation (drop in level) of the sound in traveling from A to B.

$$\text{dB} = 20 \log\left(\frac{d_1}{d_2}\right) = 20 \log\left(\frac{300}{4}\right) = 20 \log(75)$$

$$= 20 \times (1.875) = 37.5 \text{ dB}$$

The SPL at B is then 128 - 37.5 = 90.5 dB. If we solve this same problem by use of Rule 2, i.e., for every doubling of the distance we attenuate 6 dB, we can write:

```
at   4 ft  SPL  =  128 dB  (given)
at   8 ft  SPL  =  122 dB  (drop 6 dB)
at  16 ft  SPL  =  116 dB  (drop 6 dB)
at  32 ft  SPL  =  110 dB  (drop 6 dB)
at  64 ft  SPL  =  104 dB  (drop 6 dB)
at 128 ft  SPL  =   98 dB  (drop 6 dB)
at 256 ft  SPL  =   92 dB  (drop 6 dB)
at 512 ft  SPL  =   86 dB  (drop 6 dB)
```

and by interpolation at 300' we get 90.5 dB. Using the second rule in this case did not save time, because there were too many steps of computation to go through. Many sound system designers use this rule exclusively for all attenuation problems, even though correct for outdoor use only. At this point the reader may ask if an SPL of 90.5 dB at the listener location is loud enough to be heard easily. Table 8-3 is a guide to some common sound pressure levels of the human voice.

Our listener in Example 3 evidently will hear quite well under favorable ambient conditions with a sound pressure level of 90.5 dB. It is interesting now to turn our attention to the relationship between the sound pressure level created by the loudspeaker and the watts of power that the speaker must receive from the amplifier to produce this SPL.

Example 3

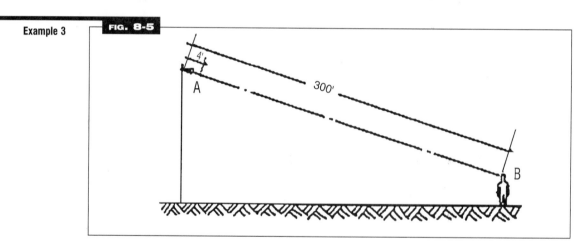

FIG. 8-5

Loudspeaker input power required

Loudspeakers are rated by the manufacturer to provide the designer with a performance criterion known as "sensitivity." It is expressed as a sound pressure level measured on axis, at a specified distance from the loudspeaker, and with a given power input of pink noise band-limited for the system under test. If the loudspeaker is a sub woofer, then it is tested only on the very low frequencies. However, if the loudspeaker is a full range system it will be tested over a much wider frequency range. The standard distance usually is 1 m (approximately 3'), and the power input usually is 1 watt. Pink noise refers to the uniform filtered output of a signal generator, whereby the output is essentially flat, producing an equal energy level per 1/3 octave band. If a pink noise filter is not used, the signal generator will produce "white noise," which is equal energy level at all frequencies and displays a rising characteristic of 3 dB/octave on 1/3-octave real time analyzers. Pink noise is used solely for the convenience of measurement.

If we know the manufacturer's sensitivity rating for a given loudspeaker measured at 1m with a 1-watt input, we can compare this with the sound pressure level required at that point to produce the required SPL at the furthest listener location. We can then calculate how much power above the 1-watt level we need to produce the required SPL.

Example 4

Figure 8-6 depicts a horn installation, outdoors, with a typical pole-mounted horn aimed to cover listeners up to 400' away in a certain direction. The goal is to reach the furthest listener with an SPL of 83 dB. An available horn can produce 114 dB-SPL @ 4' and 1-watt input. Its driver is rated to handle 100 watts of audio power. Will it do the job?

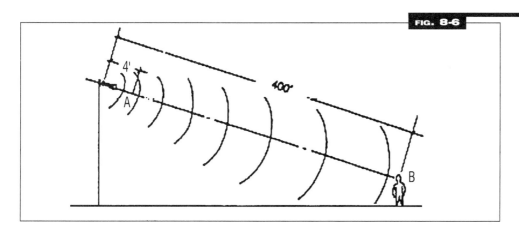

FIG. 8-6   Example 4

TABLE 8-3 Common sound pressure levels of the human voice

Sound pressure

Human Voice	N/m² at 1 foot distance	dB-SPL at 1 foot distance
Average whisper	0.0002	20
Loud whisper	0.01	54
Normal voice	0.1	74
Loud voice	0.5	88
Shout	1	94

Solution:

Attenuation between points A and B:

$$\text{attenuation} = 20\log\left(\frac{400}{4}\right) = 20\log(100)$$

$$= 20(2) = 40 \text{ dB}$$

SPL at listener's location (given)   =   83 dB

SPL required at point A   =   123 dB

Note: It is customary to add 10 dB to account for the additional power delivered at the peaks of the sinusoidal audio sound waves, inasmuch as the sound pressures involved in our audio measurements are RMS (root mean square) values, and not peak sine-wave values. This additional power is sometimes referred to as headroom.

$$\text{Total SPL at A} = 123 + 10 = 133 \text{ dB}$$
$$\text{Sensitivity of given horn} = 114 \text{ dB}$$
$$\text{SPL above 1 watt } (133 - 114) = 19 \text{ dB}$$

Now we have a simple case of expressing the comparison between two powers in decibel notation. We have already seen that power levels are compared in decibel notation by the relationship

$$\text{dB-PWL} = 10 \log\left(\frac{P_1}{P_2}\right)$$

where,

P$_1$ is the larger of the two powers

P$_2$ is the given power, 1 watt,

dB-PWL is the power level required above 1 watt

Substitution of the known values gives:

$$133\text{-}114 = 10 \log\left(\frac{P_1}{1}\right)$$

$$\frac{19}{10} = \log\left(\frac{P_1}{1}\right)$$

$$\log(P_1) = 1.9$$

from which $P_1 = 10^{1.9} = 79.4$ watts.

Note: Raising the base 10 to the 1.9 power is called finding the antilog. Thus, the antilog of 1.9 is 79.4. Put another way, 79.4 is the number whose logarithm to the base 10 is 1.9. Remember the basic definition of a logarithm: A logarithm is an exponent (1.9) to which some number called the base (10) must be raised to produce the given number (79.4). Thus, $10^{1.9} = 79.4$.

The horn selection is found to be satisfactory. An amplifier with an output of 150 watts would be a good choice. Loudspeakers are rated by average power, not peak power, so it is better to have the power amplifier a little bigger than the loudspeaker rating.

Working with sound pressure levels indoors

The behavior of sound in a reverberant space is a complicated process to analyze. While the mathematical derivations and physics involved in the various formulas that have been developed over the years are beyond the scope of this text, those most frequently needed will be given, and their use explained. Supporting data is given, although necessarily in brief, to permit intelligent use of the information. The knowledge of logarithms, decibel notation, sound pressure levels and so forth is a necessary prerequisite to understanding the various processes. Typical problems are given, along with suggested methods of solution. In an effort to keep relevant information keyed to a particular type of problem, the problem will form the text. Figures 8-10, 8-11, and 8-13 are devoted to the problems, with calculations in the left column, and data and equations in the right, developed as the problems progress. Before working on the problems, readers should review some basic definitions. They are as follows:

The direct sound field

The sound field in a room, produced by a single source such as a loudspeaker, may be thought of as divided into two parts. The first part is that portion of the field relatively near to the sound source, where the listener can hear the direct sound before it has been reflected from the surrounding walls, ceiling and other surfaces. Such locations are said to be in the direct field of the sound source. A characteristic of the direct field is that the sound pressure level attenuates, or declines, as it does outdoors, dropping 6 dB for every doubling of the distance from the emitter. This is the inverse square law at work, where the attenuation is

$$20 \log \frac{d_1}{d_2} \text{ dB.}$$

The reverberant field

The second part of the sound field is the area that lies beyond the direct field. Here the sound pressure level drops very little, because it now is reinforced by all the reflective surfaces that the sound waves have encountered in their path of travel. As a matter of fact, the sound pressure level may remain essentially constant over large areas remote from the source.

The attenuation of sound indoors is given by the equation

$$10 \log \left[\frac{Q}{4\pi^2} + \frac{4}{R} \right] \text{dB,}$$

where,

$\dfrac{Q}{4\pi^2}$ term accounts for the direct radiation,

$\dfrac{4}{R}$ term accounts for the room absorption.

The term $4\pi r^2$ is the surface area of a hypothetical sphere of radius r, the distance from the source to the point where we wish to know the attenuation. This equation is complicated by the inclusion of the acoustic parameters Q and R, which are defined next.

Directivity factor Q

Q is a dimensionless ratio comparing the amount of acoustic power radiated by a directional source, such as a horn, to that which is radiated by a non-directional source of the same acoustic power, radiating into a spherical pattern. The value of Q naturally depends on the type of directional device under consideration. Efficiently shaped multicellular horns have a higher Q than a cone-type loudspeaker. The human mouth forms a directive source with a rather low Q value. Typical values are given in Table 8-4.

TABLE 8-4 Typical values of directivity factor Q

Source	Q
Omnidirectional source suspened from a ballon	1
Omnidirectional source on the ground	2
Person talking, no sound system used	2-2.5
Omnidirectional source on the ground against the side of a building	4
Coaxial loudspeaker in infinite baffle. (Typical home hi-fi speaker)	5
Cone type woofer	5
Directional loudspeakers	5 - 9.5

Room constant R

The room constant R is a handy single-number index of the "livens" of a given room. It depends on the acoustical treatment of the walls, ceiling and floor, and on any other sound-absorbing elements within the room such as occupants and upholstered furniture.

Each kind of wall surface, or object, has its own characteristics in the way it absorbs or reflects sound. The sound-absorbing efficiency of the surface involved is given in terms of an absorption coefficient designated by the symbol α, which is the Greek letter alpha. This coefficient tells us simply what percentage of the sound striking the surface is absorbed. If a wall material has an absorption coefficient of 0.26, it means that 26 percent of the sound energy striking the surface is absorbed. An open window reflects no sound, all of it being absorbed by the air in the opening. Hence its absorption coefficient is 1.0, meaning 100 percent of the sound is absorbed. A thick, painted concrete bunker wall will reflect all of the sound back into the room, so it has an absorption coefficient of 0.0. Obviously the absorption coefficient can vary from 0.0 to 1.0.

Practically, sound absorption coefficients are obtained by measuring the time-rate of decay of the sound energy density in an approved reverberant room, with and without a patch of the sound absorbent material laid on the floor. Most published coefficients are found in this manner, and are referred to as α_{sab}. The letters sab stand for sabines, named after Wallace Clement Sabine (1868-1919), who discovered that the reverberation time for a room was dependent on its volume and the absorbtivity of its interior surfaces and objects.

Table 8-5 is an abbreviated table of sound absorption coefficients. Note that α varies with the frequency of the sound, but in practical calculations the 500Hz value usually is used.

In use, the area of each kind of surface is multiplied by its absorption coefficient. The product is expressed in sabines.

In calculations involving sound fields in reverberant spaces we must find the average absorption coefficient designated as $\bar{\alpha}_{sab}$, pronounced alpha bar sabine. This is found by summing all the products of surface S and corresponding $\bar{\alpha}_{sab}$, then dividing by the total surface of the interior space, including walls, floor, ceiling and any irregular shapes. Due to the difficulty of measuring the area of occupants, upholstered chairs and so forth, Table 8-5 gives values in sabines per person or seat. The product of persons or seats times the sabines per person or seat may be added to the above sum of $S\alpha$, the total sum to be divided by the total S to arrive at $\bar{\alpha}_{sab}$, the average Sabine absorption coefficient. In practical applications the room constant R may be found from

$$R = S\bar{\alpha}_{sab} \quad ft^2$$

Note that R has the units of square feet, since α is dimensionless.

Reverberation time

The reverberation time, with symbol RT_{60}, indicates the time in seconds for an initial sound in a reverberant space to drop 60 dB in sound pressure level, or to die away to 1-millionth of its original intensity.

A space with a short reverberation time, such as 0.2 second, is a "dead" space. An RT_{60} of 3 seconds would indicate an extremely live space, such as a large-volume stone church. The longer the reverberation time, the more difficult speech articulation becomes. Speech-destroying echoes are associated with long reverberation times, whereas dead spaces with short reverberation times require electronic voice enhancement to ensure good speech intelligibility. The curves in Figure 8-7 show typical reverberation times for various space categories, versus the enclosed volume of the space.

TABLE 8-5 Condensed list of sound absorption coefficients

Material	Sound absorption coefficients Frequency, Hz 1/1 Octave Band Center Frequency					
	125	250	500	1000	2000	4000
Brick, unglazed	0.03	0.03	0.03	0.04	0.05	0.07
Concrete block, painted	0.10	0.05	0.06	0.07	0.09	0.08
Glass, heavy plate	0.18	0.06	0.04	0.03	0.02	0.02
Glass, typical window	0.35	0.25	0.18	0.12	0.07	0.04
Gypsum Board, 1/2", on studs	0.29	0.10	0.05	0.04	0.07	0.09
Plaster, on lath	0.14	0.10	0.06	0.05	0.04	0.03
Plywood , 3/8" paneling	0.28	0.22	0.17	0.09	0.10	0.11
Concrete block, coarse	0.36	0.44	0.31	0.29	0.39	0.25
Cork, 1", with air space	0.14	0.25	0.40	0.25	0.34	0.21
Lightweight drapes, full	0.03	0.04	0.11	0.17	0.24	0.35
Medium weight drapes, full	0.07	0.31	0.49	0.75	0.70	0.60
Heavy weight drapes, full	0.14	0.35	0.55	0.72	0.70	0.65
Concrete or terrazzo	0.01	0.01	0.02	0.02	0.02	0.02
Cork, rubber pvc, on concrete	0.02	0.03	0.03	0.03	0.03	0.02
Wood parquet on concrete	0.04	0.04	0.07	0.06	0.06	0.07
Carpet, heavy, on concrete	0.02	0.06	0.14	0.37	0.60	0.65
Carpet, heavy, on foam rubber	0.08	0.24	0.57	0.69	0.71	0.73
Indoor-outdoor carpet	0.01	0.05	0.10	0.20	0.45	0.65
Gypsum board, thick	0.29	0.10	0.05	0.04	0.07	0.09
Acoustic tile, 3/4", suspended	0.76	0.93	0.83	0.99	0.99	0.94
Sprayed cellulose fibers	0.08	0.29	0.75	0.98	0.93	0.76
Air absorption, 50% relative. humidity	0.9 sabines per 1000 cubic feet					
Audience + lightly upholstered seats	4.5 sabines per seat					

FIG. 8-7

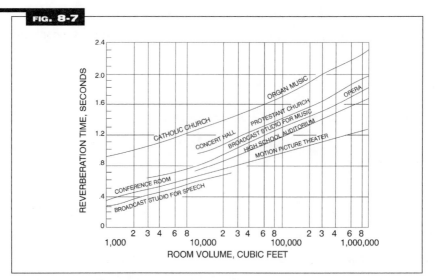

Several equations have been developed for the calculation of reverberation time, but for our purpose the well-known Sabine equation will be used, where

$$RT_{60} = \frac{0.049 \times \text{volume of space } (ft^3)}{\text{total sabines of absorption}}$$

Let us now apply these brief acoustical procedures to an elementary problem.

Example 5:
Acoustical calculations,
lecture hall

FIG. 8-8

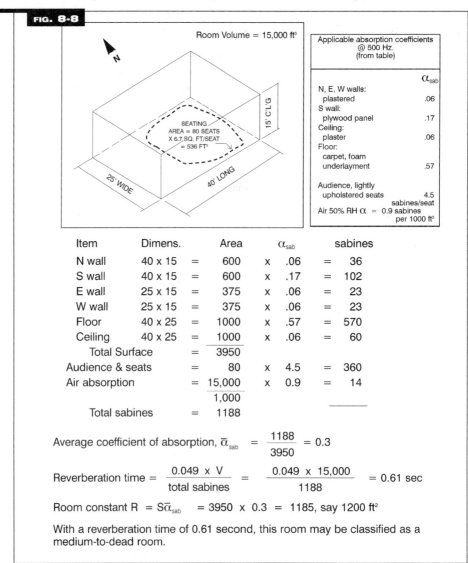

Room Volume = 15,000 ft³

Applicable absorption coefficients @ 500 Hz. (from table)	
	α_{sab}
N, E, W walls:	
plastered	.06
S wall:	
plywood panel	.17
Ceiling:	
plaster	.06
Floor:	
carpet, foam underlayment	.57
Audience, lightly upholstered seats	4.5 sabines/seat
Air 50% RH α = 0.9 sabines per 1000 ft³	

SEATING AREA = 80 SEATS X 6.7 SQ. FT/SEAT = 536 FT²

15' CLG
25' WIDE
40' LONG

Item	Dimens.		Area		α_{sab}		sabines
N wall	40 x 15	=	600	x	.06	=	36
S wall	40 x 15	=	600	x	.17	=	102
E wall	25 x 15	=	375	x	.06	=	23
W wall	25 x 15	=	375	x	.06	=	23
Floor	40 x 25	=	1000	x	.57	=	570
Ceiling	40 x 25	=	1000	x	.06	=	60
Total Surface		=	3950				
Audience & seats		=	80	x	4.5	=	360
Air absorption		=	15,000 / 1,000	x	0.9	=	14
Total sabines		=	1188				

Average coefficient of absorption, $\overline{\alpha}_{sab} = \dfrac{1188}{3950} = 0.3$

Reverberation time $= \dfrac{0.049 \times V}{\text{total sabines}} = \dfrac{0.049 \times 15,000}{1188} = 0.61$ sec

Room constant R $= S\overline{\alpha}_{sab} = 3950 \times 0.3 = 1185$, say 1200 ft²

With a reverberation time of 0.61 second, this room may be classified as a medium-to-dead room.

We now are ready to examine the attenuation of sound as it travels from a horn loudspeaker source at one end of a room to a remote listener at the far end of the room, and define the direct and the reverberant sound fields. This will be done by calculating the attenuation at successive increments of distance, from 1' to 120' from the horn loudspeaker, and plotting a graph of the results.

We will choose a room with medium-live characteristics, with a reverberation time of about 1.75 seconds, and having dimensions of 125' long x 75' wide x 24' high. The design data for this space is

$$V = 125 \times 75 \times 24 = 225,000 \text{ ft}^3$$
$$S = 28,350 \text{ ft}^2$$
$$\bar{\alpha}_{sab} = 0.22$$
$$RT_{60} = 1.75 \text{ sec}$$
$$R = S\bar{\alpha}_{sab} = 28,350 \times .22 = \text{approx. } 6,300 \text{ ft}^2$$
For the horn loudspeaker, $Q = 6$

Taking incremental distances, r, we can calculate the dB attenuation for each distance, using the attenuation formula given for reverberant spaces.

$$\text{For r } = 1 \text{ ft, attenuation } = 10 \log \left[\frac{6}{4\pi(1)^2} + \frac{4}{6300} \right] = -3.2 \text{ dB}$$

$$
\begin{array}{lcl}
r = 2 \text{ ft} & = & -9.2 \\
r = 4 \text{ ft} & = & -15.2 \\
r = 8 \text{ ft} & = & -20.92 \\
r = 10 \text{ ft} & = & -22.67 \\
r = 20 \text{ ft} & = & -27.38 \\
r = 40 \text{ ft} & = & -30.3 \\
r = 80 \text{ ft} & = & -31.6 \\
r = 100 \text{ ft} & = & -31.7 \\
r = 120 \text{ ft} & = & -31.8 \\
\end{array}
$$

The graph in Figure 8-9 plotted on semi-logarithmic graph paper (the horizontal scale is logarithmic and the vertical scale is linear) shows how the sound pressure level reaches a constant value in the reverberant field.

Critical distance

If we equate the direct radiation term

$$\frac{Q}{4\pi r^2}$$

and absorption term

$$\frac{4}{R}$$

in the attenuation equation given above, we can solve for r, which will tell us at what distance from the sound source the direct and reverberant fields have the same attenuation. This distance is known as the critical distance, D_c. Its value will be

$$\frac{Q}{4\pi r^2} = \frac{4}{R}$$

$$16\pi r^2 = QR$$

$$r^2 = \frac{QR}{16\pi}$$

$$D_C = r = \sqrt{\frac{QR}{16\pi}} = 0.141 \sqrt{QR}$$

Critical distance calculations

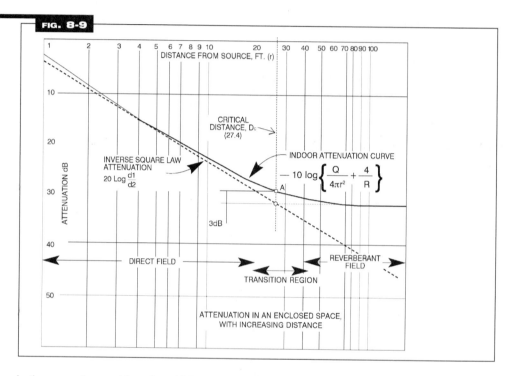

FIG. 8-9

In the preceding problem, for which we have drawn the attenuation curve, the critical distance is

$$D_C = 0.141 \sqrt{6 \times 6300} = 27.4 \text{ ft}$$

Examination of the graph shows that we can arrive at the same answer by noting that at 27.4' the direct, or free field, attenuation (inverse square law) drops to the lowest level of the reverberant field curve. It is important to remember also that when we add two equal sound pressure levels together, the sum is 3 dB greater. In other words, when we say that the free-field sound pressure level drops to the level of the sound pressure in the reverberant field, we are combining two equal sound pressure levels, and the resultant level is 3 dB higher, as shown in Figure 8-9 by point A on the indoor attenuation curve.

The room space between the source and the critical distance is known as the free, or direct, field, and that which lies beyond is called the reverberant field. Actually there is not a sharp line of demarcation between the two fields, and there is an area of transition lying between them. These fields are approximated on the Figure 8-9 graph.

The significance of the critical distance is first of all that it represents a sound pressure level within 3 dB of the maximum acoustical separation between a microphone and a loudspeaker that can ever be obtained in a given reverberant room. Once beyond the critical distance, a roving microphone would not be vulnerable to feedback. Hence the critical distance has a distinct importance where microphone and loudspeaker systems are being designed.

A workable relationship in reverberant rooms with voice amplification is that the distance from the loudspeaker to the microphone should equal or exceed the critical distance, but should not be greater than 45'.

In more reverberant spaces, with reverberation times exceeding 1.6 seconds, the distance from the loudspeaker to the farthest listener should not exceed about 3 D_c. When it does, articulation loss increases. In spaces where there is no voice amplification system, the sound from a program loudspeaker can cause no feedback, but attenuation beyond the critical distance continues in accordance with the double distance/6 dB rule, while the reverberant sound pressure level remains constant, or virtually so. At twice D_c, which is 54.8', there is a 6-dB drop from the indoor attenuation curve to the inverse square law attenuation line. At twice 54.8', or 109.6' ($4D_c$), articulation will suffer and hearing will become difficult, due to the 12-dB drop that has accumulated by twice doubling the distance. In other words, the direct sound level has dropped 12 dB below the reverberant sound pressure level. Four times the critical distance is the maximum distance at which any listener should be expected to hear with good intelligibility.

The following problems are typical of those encountered in practice, and are handled in sufficient detail to enable the reader to develop a methodical approach to a solution. The first problem, called Typical Problem A, concerns a speaker system centrally located above or behind a projection screen to transmit prerecorded sound from film sound tracks, audiotape, disks and so forth, to an audience area in a reverberant space. Situations like this are typical of small theaters, auditoriums, lecture halls, screening rooms and seminar rooms, where the program audio system is separate from the voice reinforcement system.

The object of the analysis is to determine the proper loudspeaker performance so that a listener in the rear of the room will hear the program material at the proper level, and without appreciable loss of articulation. The necessary amplifier wattage also will be investigated.

As we have seen in previous examples, certain acoustical parameters of the space must be known, or calculated. This information will be assumed or developed as needed.

FIG. 8-10

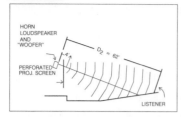

Given:
Small auditorium, volume = 125,000 ft².
Sensitivity of proposed loudspeaker = 99 dB - SPL @ 4 ft and 1 watt
Loudspeaker Q = 5
Assume RT_{60} = 1.2 seconds. This value is recommended for a space midway between "High School Auditorium" and "Motion Picture Theater" on the graph shown in Fig.8-7.
Speaker used for program only Analyze the speaker performance.

Solution:
Step 1.
Assume a sound pressure level at remote listener's location.

Supporting Data:
Assume dB-SPL = 88 @ 62 ft
See Table 8-1.

Step 2.
Find attenuation between loudspeaker and listener.

$$R = \frac{0.049 \times 125,000}{1.2 \text{ sec}} = 5104 \text{ ft}^2$$

$$\Delta_{62'} = 10 \log \left[\frac{5}{4\pi(62)^2} + \frac{4}{5104} \right]$$

$$= 10 \log (0.0008872)$$
$$= -30.52 \text{ dB. Minus sign indicates loss.}$$

$$\Delta_{D_2} = 10 \log \left[\frac{Q}{4\pi r^2} + \frac{4}{R} \right] \text{ dB}$$

where,

Δ_{D_2} = attenuation over distance D_2
$r = D_2 = 62$ ft
$Q = 5$ (given)
$$R = \frac{0.049 \, V}{RT_{60}}$$

Step 3.
Find attenuation 4 ft from loudspeaker.

$$\Delta_{4'} = 10 \log \left[\frac{5}{4\pi(4)^2} + \frac{4}{5104} \right]$$

$$= -15.91 \text{ dB}$$

$$\Delta_D = 10 \log \left[\frac{Q}{4\pi r^2} + \frac{4}{R} \right] \text{ dB}$$

where,

$r = D = 4$ ft

Step 4.
Find net attenuation between 4-ft measuring point and listener location.

Net atten. = 30.52 − 15.91
= 14.6 dB

$$\text{Net } \Delta_{62'-4'} = \Delta_{62'} - \Delta_{4'}$$

Step 5.
Add insertion loss due to passing sound through a perforated screen.

Insertion loss = 1 dB
Add peaking factor = 10 dB

Step 6.
Find operating SPL required at 4-ft standard rating distance from loudspeaker.

SPL = 14.6 + 1 + 10 + 88
= 113.6 dB

Insertion loss is omitted when loudspeaker is not located behind perforated screen.

Peaking factor allows for sine wave peaks that are present in sound reproduction, especially music.

SPL = net attenuation +
insertion loss +
peaking factor +
listener level

Step 7.
Find the dB above the 1-watt sensitivity produced by the loudspeaker, required to reach the value found in Step 6.

This is simply the difference between the required SPL and the rated 1-watt SPL of the loudspeaker.

continued on next page

Step 8. Find electric power required to produce the increase of Step 7, above 1 watt. $EPR = (10)^{\frac{14.6}{10}} = 10^{1.46}$ $= 28.8$ watts Use a 50-watt amplifier	Let $EPR = P_1$ and 1 watt $= P_2$. Then 14.6 dB PWL $= 10 \log \dfrac{P_1}{P_2}$ $= 10 \log \dfrac{P_1}{1}$ $\log P_1 = \dfrac{14.6}{10}$ from which $P_1 = (10)^{\frac{14.6}{10}}$
Step 9. Check that the maximum listener distance D_2 is less than $4D_c$. $62' < 4(22.5')$ $< 90'$ O.K.	D_c = critical distance as found previously $D_c = 0.141 \sqrt{QR}$ $= 0.141 \sqrt{5 \times 5,104}$ $= 22.5'$
Step 10. Check for minimum Q required for articulation loss of consonants not to exceed 15%. $Q_{min} = \dfrac{641.81(62)^2(1.2)^2}{15 \times 125,000} = 2$ Given $Q = 5$ O.K.	$Q_{min} = \dfrac{641.81(D_2)^2(RT_{60})^2}{15 \times V}$ where, 641.81 is a constant. $D_2 = 62'$ $RT_{60} = 1.2$ sec $V = 125,000$ ft³

The next problem, Typical Problem B, involves the use of a proscenium-mounted loudspeaker system covering the entire audience area and used for voice reinforcement only. There is a stage microphone mounted on a lectern, and a push-to-talk microphone used in the audience area. If a program speaker were also required, it would be a separate system similar to Typical Problem A. In this application, feedback is possible because we have an open microphone on the stage, which can hear the loudspeaker that is transmitting the amplified voice of the talker.

The loudspeaker should be able to transmit the amplified voice of the talker with sufficient SPL to reach the farthest listener with the same sound level that a person near the talker would experience if there were no amplification system in use.

The placement of the loudspeaker is extremely important, because its SPL, attenuated off-axis over distance D_1, in figure 8-11, may exceed the SPL of the talker's voice at the microphone. When these two sound pressure levels are equal, the condition is called unity gain. Beyond unity gain the system is vulnerable to feedback and howl at certain frequencies.

In this problem, we introduce the term *equivalent acoustic distance*, EAD. This is the distance, measured from the talker, at which the farthest listener thinks the talker is located when the sound system is in use. It varies between 3' and 20', depending on how noisy the ambient space is and how well the listener hears.

FIG. 8-11

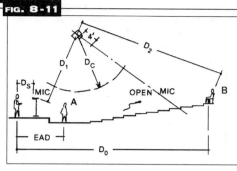

Given distances:
D_0 = 62'
D_1 = 22'
D_2 = 52'
D_s = 2'
EAD = 8'

Given:

V = 124,000 ft³   Loudspeaker Q = 5
S = 20,000 ft²   Talker Q = 2.5 (human voice)
                       SPL of talker = 80 dB @ 1' from the lips
$\overline{\alpha}_{sab}$ = 0.18   Sensitivity of selected loudspeaker = 96 dB @ 4' and 1 watt

Analyze sound system requirements for "B" to hear with a sound system, as well as "A" does without one.

Solution:	Supporting Data:
Step 1. Calculate D_C, the critical disitance. $D_C = 0.141\sqrt{5 \times 20{,}000 \times .18}$ $D_C = 18.92'$	$D_C = 0.141\sqrt{QS\,\overline{\alpha}_{sab}}$ This distance should be less than D_1, the distance from loudspeaker to microphone.
Step 2. Calculate room constant R. R = 20,000 × 0.18 R = 3600 ft²	$R = S\overline{\alpha}_{sab}$ ft²
Step 3. Calculate reverberation time in seconds. $RT_{60} = \dfrac{0.049 \times 124{,}000}{-20{,}000\,\ln(1-0.18)}$ $RT_{60} = -1.53$ seconds	If $\overline{\alpha}_{sab}$ is greater than 0.15, the Norris-Eyring equation is recommended. $RT_{60} = \dfrac{0.049\ V}{-Sin(1 - \overline{\alpha}_{sab})}$ where, ln = natural log to the base e

Step 4.
Calculate the SPL at an 8' EAD for a talker level of 80 dB @ 1'(given)
 	
$\Delta_8' - \Delta_1' = 23.75 - 6.99 =$
    16.76
SPL @ EAD = 80 - 16.76
    = 63.24 dB
	$\Delta_8' - \Delta_1' = 10 \log \left[\dfrac{Q}{4\pi r_1{}^2} + \dfrac{4}{R} \right]$
	
	    $- 10 \log \left[\dfrac{Q}{4\pi r_2{}^2} + \dfrac{4}{R} \right]$
	where,
	Q = 2.5 (talker)
	r_1 = 8'
	r_2 = 1'
	SPL @ EAD = **80 - ($\Delta_8' - \Delta_1'$)**
	This is the acceptable level.

Step 5. Find "peak" level @ "B" SPL @ B = 63.24 + 10 = 73.24 dB	SPL @ "B" = SPL @ "A", a design goal. The 10-dB headroom allows for sine wave peaks, and is added to SPL @ "B".

Step 6.
Find attenuation from 4' measuring point, on speaker axis to farthest listener at "B".
 	
$\Delta_{52}' - \Delta_4' = 29.00 - 15.85$
    = 13.15 dB loss
	$\Delta_{52}' - \Delta_4' = 10 \log \left[\dfrac{5}{4\pi 52^2} + \dfrac{4}{3600} \right]$
	
	    $- 10 \log \left[\dfrac{5}{4\pi 4^2} + \dfrac{4}{3600} \right]$

Step 7. Find required speaker SPL @ 4'. Speaker SPL = 73.24 + 13.15 = 86.39 dB	Speaker SPL @ 4' = SPL @ B+ attenuation loss from 4' to "B"

continued on next page

Note that we are now ready to compare the potential acoustic gain, PAG, with the needed acoustic gain, NAG, to determine whether or not the system is in danger of feedback.

The PAG is the gain before feedback that the system can tolerate, and the NAG is the needed acoustic gain to make the fartlhest listener think he is as close to the talker as the EAD distance.

Step 8. Find NAG.	
NAG = 29.16 - 23.75 = 5.41 dB	$NAG = \Delta_{D_0} - \Delta_{EAD}$

$$= 10 \log \left[\frac{5}{4\pi 62^2} + \frac{4}{3600} \right] -$$

$$- 10 \log \left[\frac{5}{4\pi 8^2} + \frac{4}{3600} \right]$$

Step 9.
Find PAG.
$PAG = \Delta_{22}' - \Delta_{62}' - \Delta_{52}' - \Delta_{2}'$
      $- 6 - 10 \log 2$
    $= 27.14 + 29.16 - 29 - 9.97 - 6 - 3.01$
    $= 8.32$ dB
PAG $\geq$ NAG, therefore the system is free from feedback

$PAG = \Delta_{D_1} + \Delta_{D_0} - \Delta_{D_2} - \Delta_{D_S}$
      $- FSM - 10 \log NOM$

where,
  FSM = feedback stability margin, taken as 6 dB
NOM = number of open microphones

Each open microphone produces a drop in feedback stability.

This distance should be less than D_1, the distance from loudspeaker to microphone.

Step 10.
Calculate electric power required at the speaker input, EPR.

SPL, above or below the 1-watt value given for the speaker, is
96 - 86.39 = 9.61 dB below 1 watt

$EPR = 10 - \dfrac{9.61}{10}$
    $= .11$ watt

From Step 7, speaker SPL @ 4' = 83.39 dB

Sensitivity of given speaker = 96 dB @ 4' and 1-watt input

Note: the development of the EPR equation was given in Example 4 of this section.

It would appear that 0.11 acoustical watts is an extremely small amount of power, but in acoustic work we soon learn that 1 acoustical watt represents a lot of acoustic power. When turned up as loud as is comfortable, the average large living room hi-fi set, connected to 75-watt to100-watt amplifiers, is delivering only 0.5 acoustical watts to the loudspeakers. And such speakers are very inefficient.

In the given problem we are asking for only 63.24 dB at the farthest listener's location. Should this be raised by 3 dB, the power requirements would double. And should the loudspeaker be less efficient, the power would increase further.

In practice, it would be normal to use a 50-watt amplifier in this application. This accomplishes two things: It guarantees a higher-quality amplifier, and it provides ample headroom for power peaks, as well as for increased SPL at the farthest listener location.

In the last problem, Typical Problem C, we look at the design features of a low-level, distributed sound system using ceiling-mounted loudspeakers. Conference and meeting rooms that are small-to-medium in size, that is, up to about 28' in length, and are not overly "dead" acoustically, do not normally need a voice reinforcement system. However, when meeting rooms have to accommodate large groups of people, whether seated auditorium style, at tables or in structured groups for seminar work sessions, it becomes difficult to hear presenters who are trying to communicate with the entire audience. Some kind of voice amplification or, more correctly, voice reinforcement, is required. This situation should not be confused with a PA (public address) system.

Typical Problem C (see page 8.31) is found in small auditoriums, lecture halls, conference rooms, and so forth, where ceiling heights are usually under 15' and ceiling mounted, loudspeaker systems are indicated.

With a PA system, the listeners do not necessarily see the talker; many times they are just listening to announcements. In the voice-reinforcement situation the listeners see the talker and are able to hear the talker's remarks with natural sound, regardless of their listening distance. In order to achieve uniform sound distribution, hot spots must be avoided. This requires that an ample number of loudspeakers be used, located overhead so that circular patterns of sound overlap at the hearing level. For optimum distribution of the full range of important frequencies, overlap of as much as 50 percent in adjacent loudspeaker distribution patterns is recommended. The lower the ceiling, the more speakers are required, and vice versa. No speaker should be expected to produce a cone of sound exceeding a 120-degree coverage pattern where high intelligibility is desired.

While some manufacturers' data shows cone angles up to 120 degrees, such wide dispersion is not optimum for speech. Speech intelligibility depends on uniform ear-level coverage by the higher frequencies, and these tend to beam in smaller cone angles. When good articulation and intelligibility is not important, in background music systems, for example, the loudspeakers may be placed much farther apart.

Ceiling loudspeaker placement   FIG. 8-12

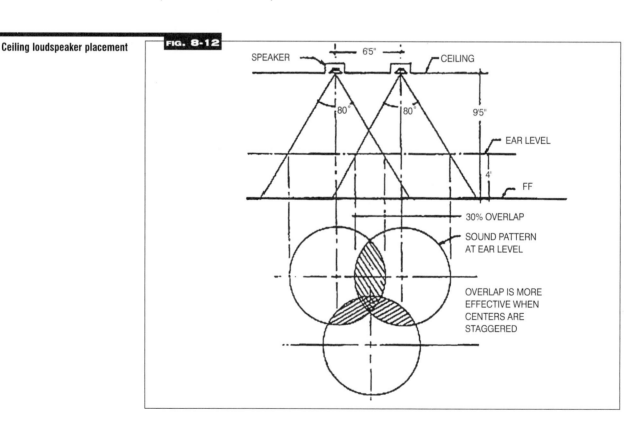

TABLE 8-6 Distance between ceiling loudspeakers
50 percent overlap* at plane of ear (seated listener)
(1.5 dB variation)

LOUD-SPEAKER ANGLE OF COVERAGE	Ceiling Height (feet and inches)													
	8'-6"	9'-0"	9'-6"	10'-0"	10'-6"	11'-0"	11'-6"	12'-0"	12'-6"	13'-0"	13'-6"	14'-0"	14'-6"	15'-0"
60°	2'-7"	2'-10"	3'-2"	3'-6"	3'-9"	4'-1"	4'-4"	4'-7"	4'-11"	5'-2"	5'-6"	5'-9"	6'-1"	6'-4"
70°	3'-2"	3'-6"	3'-10"	4'-2"	4'-7"	4-11"	5'-3"	5'-7"	6'-0"	6'-4"	6'-8"	7'-0"	7'-4"	7'-8"
80°	3'-9"	4'-2"	4'-7"	5'-0"	5'-6"	5'-11"	6'-4"	6'-9"	7'-2"	7'-7"	8'-0"	8'-5"	8'-10"	9'-3"
90°	4'-6"	5'-0"	5'-6"	6'-0"	6'-6"	7'-0"	7'-6"	8'-0"	8'-6"	9'-0"	9'-6"	10'-0"	10'-6"	11'-0"
100°	5'-4"	6'-0"	6'-7"	7'-2"	7'-10"	8'-4"	8'-11"	9'-6"	10'-2"	10'-9"	11'-4"	11'-11"	12'-6"	13'-2"
110°	6'-5"	7'-2"	7'-10"	8'-7"	9'-3"	10'-0"	10'-9"	11'-5"	12'-2"	12'-10"	13'-7"	14'-4"	15'-0"	15'-9"
120°	7'-10"	8'-8"	9'-6"	10'-5"	11'-4"	12'-2"	13'-0"	13'-10"	14'-9"	15'-7"	16'-6"	17'-4"	18'-2"	19'-1"

* Overlap is measured on the diameter of loudspeaker coverage pattern.

TABLE 8-7 Distance between ceiling loudspeakers
30 percent overlap* at plane of ear (seated listener)
(3 dB variation)

LOUD-SPEAKER ANGLE OF COVERAGE	Ceiling Height (feet and inches)													
	8'-6"	9'-0"	9'-6"	10'-0"	10'-6"	11'-0"	11'-6"	12'-0"	12'-6"	13'-0"	13'-6"	14'-0"	14'-6"	15'-0"
60°	3'-7"	4'-0"	4'-5"	4'-11"	5'-3"	5'-9"	6'-1"	6'-5"	6'-10"	7'-3"	7'-8"	8'-1"	8'-6"	8'-11"
70°	4'-5"	4'-11"	5'-4"	5'-10"	6'-5"	6'-10"	7'-4"	7'-10"	8'-4"	8'-10"	9'-4"	9'-10"	10'-3"	10'-9"
80°	5'-3"	5'-10"	6'-5"	7'-0"	7'-8"	8'-3"	8'-10"	9'-5"	10'-0"	10'-7"	11'-2"	11'-9"	12'-4"	13'-0"
90°	6'-4"	7'-0"	7'-8"	8'-5"	9'-1"	9'-10"	10'-6"	11'-2"	11'-11"	12'-6"	13'-4"	14'-0"	14'-8"	15'-5"
100°	7'-6"	8'-5"	9'-3"	10'-11"	10'-11"	11'-8"	12'-5"	13'-4"	14'-2"	15'-0"	15'-10"	16'-8"	17'-6"	18'-4"
110°	9'-0"	10'-0"	11'-0"	12'-0"	13'-0"	14'-0"	15'-0"	16'-0"	17'-0"	18'-0"	19'-0"	20'-0"	21'-0"	22'-0"
120°	11'-0"	12'-2"	13'-4"	14'-7"	15'-10"	17'-0"	18'-2"	19'-4"	20'-7"	21'-10"	23'-0"	24'-3"	25'-6"	26'-8"

* Overlap is measured on the diameter of loudspeaker coverage pattern.

TABLE 8-8 Distance between ceiling loudspeakers
0 percent overlap* edge to edge coverage
at plane of ear (seated listener)(6 dB variation)

LOUD-SPEAKER ANGLE OF COVERAGE	Ceiling Height (feet and inches)													
	8'-6"	9'-0"	9'-6"	10'-0"	10'-6"	11'-0"	11'-6"	12'-0"	12'-6"	13'-0"	13'-6"	14'-0"	14'-6"	15'-0"
60	5'-3"	5'-9"	6'-3"	7'-0"	7'-6"	8'-0"	8'-9"	9'-3"	9'-9"	10'-6"	11'-0"	11'-6"	12'-0"	12'-9"
70	6'-3"	7'-0"	7'-9"	8'-6"	9'-0"	9'-9"	10'-6"	11'-3"	12'-0"	12-'6"	13'-3"	14'-0"	14'-9"	15'-6"
80	7'-6"	8'-6"	9'-3"	10'-0"	11'-0"	11'-9"	12'-6"	13'-6"	14'-3"	15'-0"	16'-0"	16'-9"	17'-5"	18'-6"
90	9'-0"	10'-0"	11'-0"	12'-0"	13'-0"	14'-0"	15'-0"	16'-0"	17'-0"	18'-0"	19'-0"	20'-0"	21'-0"	22'-0"
100	10'-9"	12'-0"	13'-0"	14'-6"	15'-6"	16'-9"	17'-9"	19'-0"	20'-3"	10'-6"	22'-6"	22'-9"	25'-0"	26'-3"
110	12'-9"	14'-3"	15'-9"	17'-0"	18'-6"	20'-0"	10'-6"	22'-9"	24'-3"	25'-9"	27'-0"	28'-6"	30'-0"	31'-6"
120	15'-6"	17'-3"	19'-0"	20'-9"	22'-6"	24'-3"	12-'6"	27'-9"	29'-6"	31'-3"	32'-9"	34'-6"	36'-3"	38'-0"

* Overlap is measured on the diameter of loudspeaker coverage pattern.

The prospect of installing loudspeakers in a ceiling, even if they are flush mounted, small in diameter (for speech), and quite unobtrusive, is certain to cause adverse comment when interior designers or architects are involved. For some reason, designers will permit air conditioning outlets, sprinkler heads and incandescent downlights throughout the ceiling in whatever numbers necessary to give proper performance, but they will object strenuously to loudspeaker grilles cluttering the ceiling.

A ceiling speaker installation is much like an incandescent downlight system. It requires sufficient fixtures to cover the occupied space below, at the plane of the ear. Table 8-6 gives center-to-center spacing for loudspeaker placement for various percentages of overlap, cone dispersion angle and ceiling height. Overlap is measured on the diameter of the cone circle where it intersects the plane of the ear. Figure 8-12 shows two adjacent ceiling speakers with 30 percent overlap and 80-degree cone pattern, mounted in a 9'-6" ceiling. From Table 8-7 we find the required center-to-center distance to be 6'5". (Tables 8-6 and 8-8 provide additional references.)

Very few installations have as many ceiling speakers as theoretically are required. This is not because it is undesirable, but rather because someone made an arbitrary decision that the ceiling contained too many speakers, and that half as many would be satisfactory.

It is appropriate to repeat here that the foregoing material dealing with the actual audio design parameters of typical types of spaces is not offered as an absolute methodology. Indeed there is considerable room for controversy among designers, acousticians and engineers. The best that can be hoped for is that readers will use the information presented, in conjunction with their own experience and knowledge, to further their understanding of the processes involved.

The discussion in this section has barely scratched the surface of the subject matter involved. Readers can recognize the complexity of the technology and realize the need for further study and investigation. To this end, a brief bibliography follows. We hope that interested readers will pursue selected material and put together methods and procedures to assist them in their audio design work.

FIG. 8-13   Typical problem C

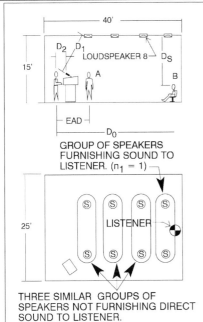

GROUP OF SPEAKERS
FURNISHING SOUND TO
LISTENER. ($n_1 = 1$)

LISTENER

THREE SIMILAR GROUPS OF
SPEAKERS NOT FURNISHING DIRECT
SOUND TO LISTENER.
($n_2 = 3$). FACTOR ($n_1 + n_2 = 1 + 3 = 4$)

Given data:
Use acoustical data from example 5.

V = 40' x 25' x 15' = 15,000 ft^3

Q = 5 for ceiling speakers

Q = 2.5 for talker

R = 1200 ft^2

RT_{60} = 0.61 sec

No. speakers = 8

Sensitivity = 88 dB-SPL at 4' and 1 watt

EAD = 4 ft = r_1

D_S = 1' = r_2

D_1 = 9' 0 "

D_2 = 11' 0" = r

D_0 = 35' 0" = r_3

Analyze loudspeaker selection and find electric power required.

Solution:
Step 1.
Calculate D_c , the critical distance.

$$D_c = 0.141 \sqrt{\frac{5 \times 1200}{4}} = 5.46'$$
$$= 5' 6"$$

Microphone is not in the direct field
of loudspeaker

Supporting Data:
D_c for a distributed sound system
may be evaluated from

$$D_c = 0.141 \sqrt{\frac{QR}{(n_1 + n_2)}}$$

Factor ($n_1 + n_2$) is explained in Fig. 7-12.

NOTE: The open microphone on the lectern is out of the direct field of the nearest loudspeaker
overhead, and should not be vulnerable to feedback. Nonetheless, the loudspeaker nearest the
lectern should be separately circuited so that it may be shut off if necessary, when the lectern microphone is in use.

Obviously the factor ($n_1 + n_2$) allows for a reduction system gain when a distributed system is used,
hence shortening D_c.

Step 2.
Establish an equivalent acoustic distance,
EAD, and calculate the dB-SPL at this
point (point "A").
Assuming the talker produces 76 dB-SPL
at the microphone ($0_S = 1'$) at EAD.
at remote listener's location.

SPL = $\Delta_{4'} - \Delta_{4'}$
= 18.02 — 6.94
= 11.06 dB

SPL @ EAD = 76 — 11.06 =
64.94

say 65 dB-SPL

The EAD should be chosen so that a satisfactory sound level exists at this point, consistent
with the noise level of the space. A 4' EAD will be
assumed.

Remember that $\Delta_{4'}$ means

$$10 \log \left[\frac{Q}{4\pi r_1^2} + \frac{4}{R} \right] \text{ - etc.}$$

where
Q = 2.5 (voice)
r_1 = 4
r_2 = 1 = D_S
R = 1200

Step 3.
Find peak level at "B," the listener's position.
The same SPL will be available at "B" as at
EAD, by definition.

dB-SPL @ "B" = 65 + 10 = 75

Add 10 dB for "head room"
on sine-wave peaks.

Step 4.
Find attenuation from 4' measuring point in
front of loudspeaker to furthest listener "B".

$\Delta_{11'} - \Delta_{4'}$ = 21.79 — 15.5
= 6.29 dB-SPL

Attenuation = $\Delta_{11'} - \Delta_{4'}$ *using*

Q = 5
R = 1200
r = 11' = D_2
r_1 = 4'

continued on next page

THE AUDIO IN AUDIOVISUAL

Step 5. Find required SPL @ 4' measuring point in front of loudspeaker to furthest listener "B" Loudspeaker SPL = 75 + 6.29 = 81.29 dB-SPL	Speaker SPL = SPL @ "B" plus attenuation from 4' to "B"
Step 6. Find needed acoustic gain, NAG NAG = 24.37 – 15.50 = 8.87 dB	$NAG = \Delta_{0_2} - \Delta_{EAD}$ using Q = 5 r_2 = D_2 = 35' r_1 = 4'
Step 7. Find potential acoustic gain, PAG. PAG = 20.84 – 24.37 – 21.79 – 3.97 – 6 = 13.45 dB PAG> NAG, therefore there should be no feedback problem.	$PAG = \Delta_{0_1} - \Delta_{0_2} + \Delta_{-\Delta 0_2} - \Delta_{0_2}$ – FSM – 10 log NOM, using r = D_2 = 11' r_1 = 4' r_2 = D_S = 1' r_3 = D_1 = 35' Q = 5 R = 1200 FSM = 6 dB NOM = 1
Step 8. Calculate electric power required SPL below 1 watt = 88 – 81.29 = 6.71 $EPR = (10)^{\frac{-6.71}{10}} = 0.21$ watt/speaker Total watts = 8 x 0.21 = 1.68 Use a 50-watt amplifier	Using sensitivity given as 88 dB-SPL @ 4' and 1 watt, and required speaker SPL from Step 5. Use 1/2-watt tap on speaker transformer. As discussed, following Typical Problem "B".

Further Reading

Beranek, L. L. 1971. *Noise and Vibration Control*. New York, NY: McGraw-Hill.

Beranek, L. L. 1993. *Acoustics*. Cambridge, MA: Bolt, Beranek and Newman.

Chiswell, B. and E. Grigg, 1971. *S Units.* Sydney: John Wiley & Sons Australia Pty Ltd.

Clifford, M. 1979. *Microphones—How They Work & How to Use Them*. Blue Ridge Summit, PA: Tab Books.

Cohen, A. B. 1978. *Hi-Fi Loudspeakers and Enclosures*. Rochelle Park, NJ: Hayden Book Company.

Davis, D. and C. Davis. 1977. *Sound System Engineering*. Indiannapolis, IN: Howard W. Sams & Company, Inc.

Davis, G., and R. Jones. 1989. *The Sound Reinforcement Handbook: Second Edition.* Milwaulkee, WI: Hal Leonard Corporation.

Doelle, L. L. 1972. *Environmental Acoustics*. New York, NY: McGraw-Hill.

Egan, M. D. 1972. *Concepts in Architectural Acoustics*. New York, NY: McGraw-Hill.

Egan, D. M. 1988. *Architectural Acoustics.* New York, NY: McGraw-Hill.

Giddings, P. 1990. *Audio Systems and Installation.* Boston, MA: Focal Press.

Harris, C. M., ed. 1991. *Handbook of Acoustical Measurements and Noise Control: Third Edition.* New York, NY: McGraw-Hill.

Lord, H. W., W. S. Gatley, and H. A. Evensen. 1980. *Noise Control for Engineers.* New York, NY: McGraw-Hill.

Rettinger, M. 1977. *Acoustic Design and Noise Control, Vol. 1*. New York, NY: Chemical Publishing Company.

Rossing, T. D. 1982. *The Science of Sound.* Reading, MA: Addison-Wesley.

Tremaine, H. 1969. *Audio Cyclopedia*. Indianapolis, IN: Howard W. Sams & Company.

Wood, A. 1961. *The Physics of Music*. New York: Dover.

9

THE VIDEO IN

AUDIOVISUAL

edited and written by **MIKE WEEMS, CTS, MCP**

Mike Weems, CTS, MCP, is the
Senior Technical Trainer with
InFocus Corporation and is the
Program Coordinator for
InFocus University.
He can be contacted at
mikeweems@hotmail.com.

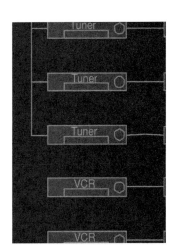

The material discussed in this section brings into focus the increasing role that video is playing in almost every kind of audiovisual facility being designed today. Its aim is to discuss video from the user's standpoint. How does the planner provide for its use? How is it applied to a given situation? How is it incorporated into modern audiovisual systems? How does its use augment conventional audiovisual projection and display techniques? How well does it perform from the standpoint of image quality, audio quality, resolution, image size, system integration, programming preparation, cost and so forth?

As with any other medium, the popularity of video in communications is directly proportional to the support it receives from television and related industries—to produce quality equipment, to provide standards of operation, to proliferate the medium in a competitive market, and to make available the accessories, services and techniques that constitute today's video needs. In this respect, the video industry has not been lacking. As a matter of comparison, it has made greater strides in less time, and at a higher technological level, than has been evident in the audiovisual industry. Computer technology has demonstrated a still faster rate of growth.

This situation is normal, for our technical growth follows the curve of learning—ever increasing. Such rapid advancement of technology in the communication field does not mean that videotape will replace film, any more than projection devices replaced the chalkboard, or television replaced the radio. It does show, however, that each new technology will impinge on all previous relevant technologies, elevating them to new standards of excellence. Thus, computers are designing superb optics for all our lens needs, microprocessors are opening up exciting control capabilities for all programmable requirements, and digital video techniques soon will provide us with an all-new concept of television signal generation and transmission.

Why video?

People use video for many reasons—to tell a story and describe an event, to sell or demonstrate a product, to teach a specific subject or instruct in a given operation, to reach a wider audience than would normally be possible, and to show things that can't be witnessed in person or are too large or small or too fast or slow to be viewed normally.

Video can play a significant role in achieving the desires and goals of a broad range of organizations. Corporations, schools, churches and government agencies all have benefited from the economies and/or expediency of video.

The video production process

This section is not intended as a primer on how to produce video, but it is hoped that a basic understanding of the steps necessary to produce video might foster a better understanding. Although not all of these steps are followed in every case, the basic concepts underlie all productions.

The process of producing a video involves the following steps:

Initial concept—development of the rough idea, possibly including designation of the target audience and the desired outcome

Scriptwriting/authoring—development of a shooting script and, in the case of an interactive presentation, development of the branching or chapter elements

Storyboarding—optional step of preparing drawings depicting each scene and/or shot in the production

Preplanning—arranging for all of the elements necessary for the production

Production—shooting of the video, recording of the audio and creation of any graphics or computer programming needed to complete the program

Post-production—combining all video, audio, graphic and computer elements into a finished product

Distribution—duplication of the finished program (the master) for distribution by whatever means

Video is distributed in many forms:
- **Baseband Video**
  CCTV or security
  Medical monitoring
- **Modulated Video**
  Television transmission
  MATV
  Cable TV
- **Computer Video**
  Mac
  PC
  Workstations
- **Video/teleconferencing**
  Over computer or phone network

Evaluation and revision—usually associated with educational programming, the evaluation of the program and possible revision to insure that the program meets the desired goals or needs.

How television came into the audiovisual scene

Educational institutions and corporations with training facilities were among the first groups of communicators to expand their audiovisual facilities to take advantage of the televised image. They used video to teach and to train. Although these users adopted television less than 30 years ago, they were pioneers.

They spent hundreds of thousands of dollars attempting to ride the wave of what was going to become the way to educate and to train. In this respect, the education community waded into the deepest water. It was motivated by the excitement and activity of exploring the learning process. Examples of such activity are the endless human behavior articles that appeared in communications and psychology magazines; the introduction of programmed self-instruction machines; the learning laboratories; the study carrel; student response systems; and, more recently, computer-assisted instruction.

In this early period of development, it was usually some educational learning laboratory that established the criteria for the "ultimate" system. And such systems often were so advanced that many of the needed devices were not commercially available, but had to be developed by a reliable manufacturer willing to risk development costs to establish a future proprietary system. A classic example of such an alliance took place in the early 1960s when a wealthy school system in a Chicago suburb introduced what was probably, at that time, the most costly and sophisticated learning system in existence. It featured individual study carrels and imme- diate dial-up random access retrieval of dozens of television tape programs displayed on individual monitors, with earphones for sound. But outside of a handful of competitive systems, the extremely expensive random access retrieval, videotape television system for individual instruction did not become the wave of the future. Few boards of education could justify the cost, and the mere passage of time was producing changes, improvements and new ideas in competitive techniques.

During the same period, industry was quick to recognize the advantage of the video image in classroom training, on-the-job training, role-playing, and the display of live televised pickup of key corporate officers addressing the employees via closed-circuit television. Such activities could profit quite naturally from the use of an in-house television studio. The late '60s and early '70s saw the rapid rise of the in-house studio, growing from an 18' x 25' black-and-white facility to a double story, fully equipped color studio 40' x 60' or larger.

Out of all this flurry of television activity, one thing remained clear: Televised teaching, training and group communication was here to stay. Its value was established not only as a medium but also as a means to an end. It came at a time when public school enrollment was burgeoning—doubling in the 20-year period prior to 1970. A teacher shortage was threatening the educational system. But by 1961 approximately 7,500 elementary and secondary schools in 600 school districts around the country were offering at least part of their regular curriculum via television. Intra-school TV exchanges among school systems were taking place with mutual benefit to all parties. Videotapes, kinescope recordings and live transmission all were used to provide the optimum mix of instructional communication.

By 1962, more than 6 million students were benefiting from televised instruction, with half that number attending classes using ITV (instructional television) and the remainder being reached by ETV (educational television). The terms ITV and ETV sometimes are used interchangeably, but there is a basic difference. The acronym ITV refers to formalized educational broadcasts that are transmitted on a planned schedule, and through which formal examinations are taken and scholastic credits earned. If the primary purpose of the material being telecast is to enhance the viewer's knowledge and general understanding of a subject, without giving credits that may be applied to earning a diploma or degree, ETV applies. The former is directed to a specific viewing group, while the latter is informal.

Some school districts made use of a "hub" school, which acted as an origination center for microwave transmission to satellite schools. A frequency of 2,500MHz was assigned to these line-of-sight systems, and they were referred to as ITFS (Instructional Television Fixed Service).

We see that there is considerable flexibility in the way that television signals can be delivered to a wide spectrum of viewers.

Baseband video distribution

One way of serving many locations within a given building is baseband video distribution. This involves the use of one or more video distribution amplifiers (DAs), which are available with up to six outputs. Audio distribution amplifiers likewise are used to distribute the audio signal, which usually is fed to a room loudspeaker system. When the television system is part of the regular audiovisual system, the two share an audio system. Although a system of this type has some advantages—mainly security—the desire to have multiple sources of programming led many to adopt radio frequency (RF) distribution systems instead.

Rf (radio frequency) distribution system

The Rf distribution system, sometimes called a modulated or broadband system, makes use of a high frequency carrier wave that is modulated, or shaped, by the video signal. Figure 9-1 depicts a typical composite of the various distribution capabilities of such a system.

Note that the devices whose outputs are video voltages, such as VCRs and video cameras, must have output signals modulated to the carrier frequency of an unused channel, so that they appear as Rf signals at the combiner, where they are combined with the local off-air channels received by the master antenna located on the roof of the building. All the Rf signals now can be distributed on a single coaxial cable to the various TV receivers (essentially monitors with built-in tuners). Where cable lengths are long and many sets are served, line amplifiers are required to make up for losses due to cable resistance and device insertion losses.

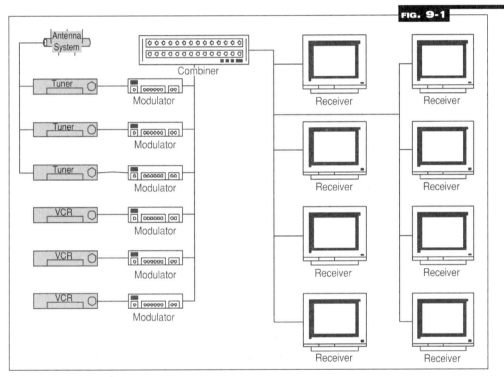

FIG. 9-1

Rf distribution system

Incorporating video into an audiovisual system

Video has many uses in today's audiovisual systems. Video cameras can be mounted on a copy stand or incorporated into a "document camera" for the projection of small objects, graphics or text-based documents. Pre-recorded video footage can be viewed from any number of sources: videotapes (VCRs) of different formats, DVDs, older laserdisc players, and even footage stored on computer hard drives or from websites, sometimes called "streaming video." And at large "staged" events, cameras are used to magnify the speaker's image while video and computer sources are blended or mixed and displayed on various screens.

Typically all of these sources are fed into some sort of switcher for selection in combination with computer sources. Additionally, the traditional NTSC standard (see below) video signals may be processed to allow them to be displayed at the same approximate resolution as the computer-based sources.

Some provision should also be made to control the function (remote control to stop, start, rewind, etc.) of the video sources. Graphical control systems typically are used for this purpose.

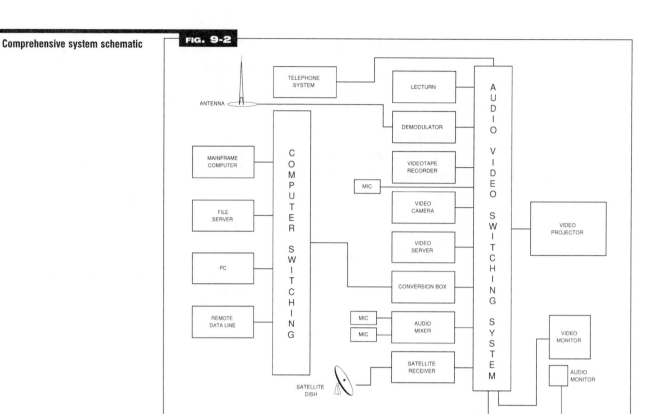

FIG. 9-2

The video signal

In the world of television various standards have been created so that the video we view, record and transmit will work in the proper manner for a given situation. In the United States, the Federal Communications Commission (FCC) has set up Standards of Transmission which guarantee that the signals transmitted by television stations will appear in their correct form on the television sets in our living rooms.

For this to happen, the cameras in the TV studio; the videotape recorders and switching and distribution devices in the control room; the television transmitters; the local cable company's headend equipment; and our television receivers all have had to be built to the same television standard. In the United States and some other parts of the world a standard called NTSC is used. It is named after the National Television System Committee, the organization that created the color television system we have for analog television transmission and production.

Different standards, such as Phase Alternate Line (PAL) or Sequential Couleur Avec Memoire (SECAM) are used in various countries around the world. These standards are totally incompatible with NTSC equipment, and with videotapes produced or television transmissions made in NTSC. Therefore it is necessary to ascertain the final destination of programming in order to determine which television transmission standard to use for production or distribution.

The basic goal of video equipment

All video equipment is designed and built with the goal of capturing and reproducing the intended scene as closely as possible to that perceived with human vision. However, certain aspects of the current video equipment take advantage of limitations in human vision.

The smallest element of the video picture is the pixel (short for picture element). The function of television is to acquire, transmit, store and/or reproduce pixels as accurately as possible from acquisition to final viewing of the recorded or transmitted picture.

Creation of the video image is the result of our understanding of human vision (the eye-brain interaction) combined with the changing physics of modern electronics.

Human limitations dictate most of what happens, while physics dictates the rest. In elementary school, we learned that human vision occurs when the rods and cones combine with image lag to create visual acuity.

The basis for the display of motion in the video signal is how motion picture images are displayed. A sequence of stills is displayed to create the illusion of motion through a phenomenon called persistence of vision. In the early days of film it was discovered that if stills were displayed at a rate of 30 frames per second (fps) or less, the image flickered. Double-gated projection of images shot at 24 fps resulted in a projected image of 48 fps, sufficient to eliminate flicker. Initially, television production (like film) was available only as a black and white (shades of gray) system.

Film is a photochemical process that produces a latent image on a transparent base. The film is its own storage device. In contrast, video is a photoconductive process that requires a separate device for storing images. Video is produced by a variable electronic signal resulting from electronic scanning.

Creating the video image

Cathode ray tubes, or CRTs, were early photoconductive pickup devices. Using CRTs, the image area was struck by electrons releasing a charge of electricity proportional to the amount of light hitting the target area. The surface area pattern is called the raster. In television the image is scanned in a horizontal pattern.

Basic scanning of the image across the raster creates the same effect as motion pictures. Standards were adopted by the FCC to cover the scanning system we have in this country.

The number of horizontal scan lines making up the raster image size was determined by studying the average viewer's ability to resolve an image at certain distances, and by applying the physics of electronic circuitry. The number arrived at was 483 lines. However, it was determined that additional lines were needed for the retrace of the electron beam from top to bottom. It was decided that 8 percent more lines were needed for retrace, yielding 525 lines—the U.S. standard.

The NTSC horizontal scanning frequency was tied to the U.S. power line rate of 60Hz. Initially 30 fps was chosen as the frame rate, but that rate was not sufficient to eliminate flicker (as in film). Thus each frame was divided into two parts (called fields); this provided 60 views per second, and eliminated flicker.

To save further on the bandwidth needed for circuitry it was decided to scan only half the fields at once. This yields a view rate of 60 fps. Each group of scanned lines is called a field. The odd lines are scanned first, then the even fields.

The vertical scan rate is the rate at which the electron beam completes X cycles of vertical motion within a second. Since the power line frequency was used to determine the field rate, it also determined the vertical scan rate—60 cycles per second (cps) or 60Hz.

The horizontal scan rate (number of lines scanned in a second) is determined by simply multiplying the number of lines in a frame by the number of frames in a second:

525 lines x 30 frames = 15,750 lines per second.

This usually is expressed 15.75kHz.

The other way to compute horizontal scan rate is to multiply the number of lines in a field (half that in a frame) by the number of fields in a second:

262.5 lines x 60 fields = 15,750 lines per second.

Resolution in a television image

The term *resolution* is used more often than it is understood. Resolution is expressed in lines, and therefore is easily confused with scan lines.

To reiterate, the American television standard is based on the use of an entire electron beam-scanning rate of 525 lines per image frame. These scan lines, which "paint" the image on the picture tube, are tilted slightly downward, starting from the center of the upper edge of the image and proceeding toward the center of the lower edge of the tube. The actual scanning process takes place in two top-to-bottom scans of 262.5 lines each. Each scan is called a field, and there are two fields per frame. The lines of the second field fall exactly between the lines of the first field. These field scans occur at an extremely rapid rate, producing 30 frames per second, or 60 fields per second.

In all there are 15,750 lines per second scanning the television raster area of the tube face (15,734 for NTSC color TV). Even though this information is traced on the tube face a line at a time, the persistence of vision of the human eye, combined with the retention qualities of the tube-coating phosphors, acts to produce a non-flickering photographic image in the brain.

Resolution lines are not an actual number of lines on the screen. Rather, the term refers to a numerical standard against which the image detail can be measured. That standard is in the form of a printed black and white chart called a test pattern. It contains, among other test configurations, a set of horizontal and vertical wedges consisting of black lines and white spaces. Figure 9-3 shows how the vertical and horizontal wedges are printed on the chart.

Partial test chart

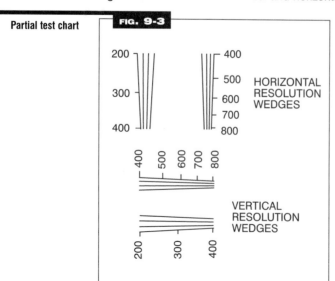

FIG. 9-3

In studio use, the camera operator focuses the camera on the chart, fills up the viewfinder's screen with the image, and adjusts its optical system for optimum sharpness by adjusting the image of each wedge seen on a technical monitor and reading the number at which the eye can no longer distinguish, or resolve, the separation between lines.

If the lines on the vertical wedge appear to merge at 320, then we are measuring a horizontal resolution of 320 lines. Likewise, if the lines on the horizontal wedge appear to converge at 340, we are measuring a vertical resolution of 340 lines.

Interpreting the lines of resolution

For resolution to have any real meaning, we have to do more than start with good resolution at the camera. The entire television system—studio cameras, tape machines, transmitters, antennas, home receivers and finally the viewers—is involved. The viewers are involved because they may not be able to use all the resolution the system can produce due to limitations of the human eye. Obviously the viewing distance, in comparison with the size of the tube being viewed, is an important factor. Assume we are looking at a 21" diagonal picture tube screen size showing 350 lines of vertical resolution on the raster, as read from the transmitted image on the test chart. This means that 350 line-pairs (a black bar and its adjacent white space) would just fill the height of the screen. The height of a 21" diagonal image is 13.75", therefore each line-pair spans a height of 13.75 divided by 350, or 0.039". This means that objects appearing 0.039" in height, a little more than 1/32", could be distinguished as individual objects, or resolved on the face of the tube in the vertical direction. But can the eye distinguish such a small object when viewing the picture tube from an average viewing distance?

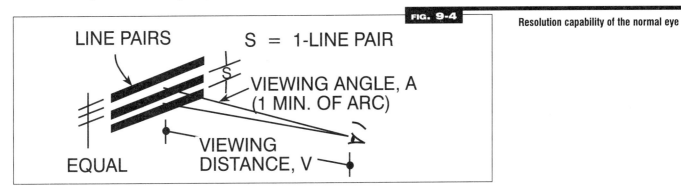

Resolution capability of the normal eye

What the eye can resolve, or distinguish

Under ideal conditions of ambient light, contrast, etc., the eye can distinguish line pairs that subtend an angle with the eye of as little as 1-minute of arc, as shown in Figure 9-5. Under average conditions, the eye has no difficulty in distinguishing objects that subtend an angle of 3-minutes of arc. Suppose we relate the viewing distance V, the viewing angle A, the tube diameter D and the object size S to find the lines of resolution useful to the eye. Because viewing distance will be expressed in terms of tube diameter so that all data developed will hold true for any size tube, we will begin by finding the relationship between the screen diameter and the screen height h.

1. The NTSC aspect ratio of the video image is 1.33:1, therefore the width of the image is 1.33h. Pythagorean theorem gives
   $SD^2 = h^2 + (1.33h)^2$ from which D = 1.664h.

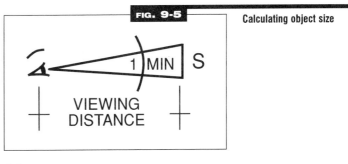

FIG. 9-5

Calculating object size

2. The lines of useful resolution, that is, the resolution that the eye can use based on average eye per-formance, are h/S, where S is found by simple trigonometry according to Figure 9-5.
   $S = \tan 1' \, (1.664Nh)*$
   $S = 0.00029088 \, (1.664Nh)$
   $S = 0.00048038Nh$
   where N is the number of tube diameters in viewing distance.

3. Lines of useful resolution =
    $h/S = h/0.00048038Nh = 2066/N$

4. Repeating steps two and three for a viewing angle of 3-minutes of arc, we find
    Lines of useful resolution = 689/N

    When dealing with small angles it is not necessary to write
    $S = 2\tan 1/2'$ (1.664Nh).

Thus, although the system is capable of producing 350 lines of vertical resolution on the face of the 21-inch television screen, our eye may be able to resolve only 295 lines with excellent vision, and when we are seated about 12' from the tube. We would be viewing the tube at a distance of 7 tube diameters.

Good viewing takes place at distances between 5 and 10 screen diameters. In large meeting rooms, viewers often are located at 12 or more screen diameters from the receiver. At these longer distances, graphics become difficult to read unless they are specially made with not more than eight lines of captions from top to bottom of the image. From the preceding considerations, it is clear that viewing distance is an important factor when we talk about resolution.

Bandwidth required for the video signal

Bandwidth is the amount of information that can be processed in the period of one second expressed in terms of frequency measured by Hz.

The average resolution of most NTSC devices is around 330 to 340 lines. This resolution results in an approximate bandwidth (total scan frequency) of 4.2MHz. Keep in mind that the greater the number of lines, the higher the bandwidth required.

More lines = Higher frequency

The Factor of 80. There are very complex formulas to help in calculating bandwidth, but to get a rough approximation engineers use the Factor or Rule of 80.

Divide the horizontal resolution by 80 to get the approximate bandwidth.
Multiply the bandwidth by 80 to get the number of lines.

NTSC signal specifications limit the video bandwidth to approximately 4 MHz.

The analog video signal

The video signal discussed to this point is an analog voltage representation of the varying levels of the different elements in the video image. These electrical voltages will vary in amount (level or amplitude) or speed (frequency).

A graphic representation of the video signal beam current is made possible by a highly specialized oscilloscope called a waveform monitor. Varying the degrees of light causes variations in the intensity of the scanning beam corresponding to picture information. Maximum beam current produces white. Zero beam current produces black. The signal can be measured by the IRE unit scale on the front of the waveform monitor (named after the Institute of Radio Engineers):

■ **IRE Scale**
140 IRE = 1 volt
100 IRE = 0.714 volt
40 IRE = 0.286 volt
IRE = .054 volt

■ **Representative levels**
Peak white = 100IRE
Pedestal = 7.5IRE
Sync = -40IRE
Burst = +20 to -20 IRE

Color television

The National Television System Committee (NTSC) was created in 1949 to establish transmission standards for color television. The NTSC report was used to define the current composite (encoded analog signal) television transmission system in the United States.

The FCC decided that any new system employing color would not totally replace and make obsolete the black and white system that existed at the time. Color systems had to be what was termed "compatible." And, as discussed earlier, the type of signal with the luminance (Y) and color (C) signals combined was called a composite video signal. This 1-volt peak-to-peak signal is made by placing the Y signal on its normal baseband carrier (approximately 4Mhz) and placing the C information on a subcarrier at approximately 3.58Mhz.

Color signal acquisition

Color television works with the additive properties of light (see the color wheel illustration on the back cover). Since every color varies in intensity and chrominance (color), incoming light is split into the three color primaries of red, green and blue (RGB). Separate imagers are required for each primary color.

To derive a 100 percent luminance value from the three color primaries, the following formula is used:

30%R + 59%G + 11%B = 100%Y

This yields the best possible color reproduction. However, due to bandwidth limitations of the circuitry, RGB signal processing is prohibitive.

The RGB signals are, therefore, matrixed to produce Y. The derived color (C) difference signals are created, and then modulated on a subcarrier at approximately 3.58MHz (or exactly 3.579545MHz). The Y and C signals then are combined to create the "composite" video signal. This color encoding is the process whereby the three color primaries are combined, allowing a camera to output the entire "mixed" signal through one cable or connector.

Standards of NTSC Transmission

The FCC has set forth the following "Standards of Transmission" governing all video signal transmissions in the United States:

■ Scanning of the raster's image will take place in horizontal lines from left to right, top to bottom, scanning 525 lines per frame at a frame rate of app. 30Hz (exactly 29.97Hz).

■ This provides the 15,734Hz scan rate for color television. The process is called interlaced scanning, since half the lines (odd lines) are scanned first, then the even ones are scanned.

- The color signal shall be placed on a subcarrier of the primary carrier at 3.579545MHz.

- The aspect ratio shall be 4 units high x 3 units across, or 1.33. The important thing to remember is that this is a ratio to be applied to whatever screen size is employed.

- The channel bandwidth shall be a maximum of 6MHz, with the picture being amplitude modulated (AM) up to 4.5MHz and the sound being frequency modulated (FM) from 4.5 up to the maximum carrier.

TV Broadcast Channel frequency assignments:
6MHz spacing between each channel
Lowband VHF – Channels 2 to 6 from 54MHz to 88MHz
Highband VHF – Channels 7 to 13 from 174MHz to 216MHz
UHF – Channels 14 to 83 from 470 to 890MHz

Signal decoding

In the modern television receiver or monitor a process exactly opposite to encoding produces a picture. This process is called decoding. The goal of decoding is reproduction of an image as close to the original as possible.

There are a number of parameters in the image that typically are controllable in these units. These picture qualities are:
Brightness
Contrast
Detail
Color level
Hue
Aspect ratio
Viewing distance

The problem with the NTSC system is that some of the built-in attributes of the system create picture "artifacts" that are not desirable, including chroma crawl and moire'. This is a result of the FCC color television compromise—fitting color onto a black and white system. To eliminate these artifacts, new technologies were developed, including component signal VTRs and, in the computer world, RGB signal generation.

Television cameras

The earliest television cameras employed tubes as the pickup devices for conversion of an image from optical to electrical. This converted the optical energy and image captured by the lens into an electrical analog equivalent. Three primary types of tubes from different manufacturers dominated the marketplace: the Vidicon, the Plumbicon and the Saticon and variations.

Solid-state pickup devices now dominate the market. A few of the more common types are:
MOS
CCDs
FT
IT
FIT
HAD CCD
Hyper-HAD CCD
PowerHAD
ExwaveHAD

Today's modern video camera comes in many configurations for many different tasks. The traditional "camera chain" usually consists of the camera head with a lens and viewfinder attached, all connected by various types of cable to a camera control unit (CCU or RCU). With the advent of one-piece camcorders (camera and recorder in one package), the need for a separate controlling electronics package was eliminated, except for multiple camera shoots (studio work and outside broadcasts, or OB). The disadvantage of these packages is that the operator becomes responsible not just for shot composition and camera movement, but for image parameter adjustment as well.

A new innovation in some modern professional broadcast or production camcorders is the capability to have both electronic news gathering (ENG) and studio configuration.

The camera head usually includes the internal optics (prism block), the electrical analog pickup devices (typically solid-state CCDs), processing circuitry and lens/viewfinder/communications. Cameras today must meet many different specifications, depending on the intended usage, and the customer's desires and needs for image capture. Among these specifications are the operating light level, depth of modulation, horizontal resolution, contrast range, and signal to noise ratio.

Most cameras allow many adjustments to be made manually and in some cases automatically, including adjustments in lens iris, circuit gain, pedestal/setup, white balance, electronic shutter, gamma, filter wheel settings and menu settings.

Selecting the right camera

Selection of a video camera depends on many factors. The first consideration is the application for the camera—surveillance, field production, studio production or another use. Since most security applications involve simply one or more cameras feeding a monitor (a gross simplification, to be sure), we will focus on the uses of cameras in the production arena.

There are many possible configurations in which to place today's modern teleproduction camera. The basic types are:

- **ENG** (electronic news gathering)
  Specifications for this camera typically are:
  One piece
  Shoulder operation
  Autos w/ manual override
  Field lenses
  DC-powered

- **EFP** (electronic field production)
  Specifications typically are:
  Two pieces—camera head and CCU
  Tripod or shoulder mounted
  CCU favors automatics
  Smaller OB lenses
  AC-DC-powered

- **ESP** (electronic studio production)

  Specifications typically are:

  Two pieces

  Pedestal mounted

  Rear cable controls (zoom and focus)

  Favors manual controls

  Automatic setup latest addition

  Extended range lenses

  CCU—AC powered in the rack

Technical considerations for cameras in a system

When adding cameras to a teleproduction system, there are a number of technical factors to consider, both at the camera location and at the terminus of the camera's signal. You may wish to invest in a few accessories for the cameras as well.

- **At the camera location:**

  Camera positioning(s)

  Camera mountings

  Communications

  Lenses—usually not the same on each in a multiple camera setup

  Power source

  Cabling and where to run it

  Microphone holder/connector

- **In the control room or truck:**

  Cable entrances or access panels

  CCU location and powering

  Intercom/tally circuits

  System timing

  Power

- **Accessories:**

  Viewfinders

  Mounting plates

  Batteries/charger

  Cases

  Raincovers

  Tool kits

  Extender cards

  Service manuals

Switching from one camera's signal to another

Video switchers are devices that allow multiple signals to be switched and mixed for output to be used for distribution and/or recording. Modern devices range from simple four-input passive security switchers up to digital production switchers with 72 or more inputs.

In order to have clean transitions (no picture disturbances) when switching and mixing among the various inputs, all video sources need to be synchronized to a single master reference generator (called a sync generator). Usually this device is a separate unit, but the switcher may have its own reference outputs for timing. The sync pulse generated by the sync generator is connected to the reference input connector (also called genlock) on the various source devices.

The sources then are "timed" by adjusting the sync (horizontal positioning of the image) and subcarrier (color phase) so that they match up.

Some pieces of video equipment (such as consumer machines) cannot be genlocked. In this case, the video output signals are sent to another device called a frame synchronizer that allows for the signal to be synchronized. Some switchers now have built-in frame synchronizers on their inputs.

In the digital domain, current switcher technology allows for "auto-timing" of signal sources, as long as the signal falls within a specified timing window. The switcher adjusts and times the signal automatically, eliminating the need for manual adjustment of sync and subcarrier. Digital switchers still require their sources to be locked to a reference (or genlock) signal.

Modern teleproduction switchers come in many different configurations. Most include rows of input selection buttons, called a "bus." Typically one bus, normally called the program bus, will select which inputs are "on-the-air." The next bus typically utilized is the preview or preset bus, so named because it lets the user preview what source is next in line to be applied to the program bus.

There may be additional buses that can be used to apply various effects to one or more source images at once. These are called mix buses.

Another type of processor and associated control is utilized in the process of "keying" one image over all or part of another image. An example of this is the superimposition of letters and graphics created by a character generator over a camera's image.

The other factor that determines the capabilities of a teleproduction switcher is the number of source inputs found on each bus. The greater the number of inputs, the more flexibility in the selection of varied sources for incorporation into a program.

The greatest capability of these switchers is the array of transitions between sources that they are capable of generating. In the early days, it was considered remarkable if a switcher could perform a split screen or even a circle wipe. But now images flip and tumble with seeming ease, thanks to the digital effects generators that are either part of a switcher or auxiliary units tied to it.

Types of switcher transitions

Modern teleproduction switchers offer a wide range of signal transitions, from a simple cut between two sources to a 3D curvilinear digital transition.

- **Cuts**
- **Dissolves and fades**
- **Wipes**
- **Keys**
    Luminance keyers
    Downstream keyers
    Chroma keyers

- **Effects**
    Basic effects—number of channels
    Digital transition
    Preprogrammed
    Programmable
    2D
    3D
    Curvilinear 3D
    Trajectory

■ **Signals**
 Analog
 Digital–4:2:2
 Serial Digital Interface(SDI)
 Serial Digital Data Interface (SDDI)

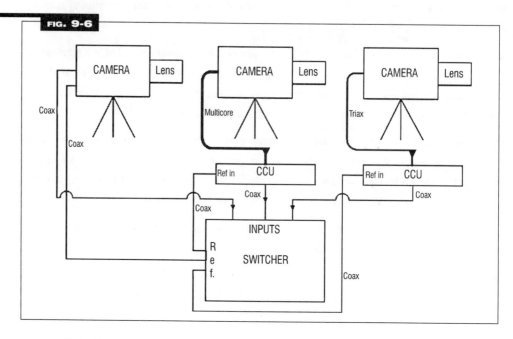

Three ways that video can flow from a camera into a switcher

FIG. 9-6

Getting signals to the switcher in the control room

The device that is used to choose between multiple video sources is called a video switcher. Figure 9-6 shows three ways for video to flow from a camera into a switcher. The simplest way is to run video from the camera back to an input on the switcher, then run a genlock signal from the sync generator (sometimes built into the switcher) back to the genlock or reference input on the camera. The user must then make adjustments to the internal timing circuits in the camera to sync it to the inputs from the other sources feeding the switcher. The problem with this approach is that the user has no remote control of camera parameters and no communications.

The second illustration shows a traditional multicore cable, which allows video, reference, return video, intercom, tally and possibly other functions to travel to and from the camera to the camera control unit (CCU), which then feeds the signal to the switcher. All signals bound for the camera go through the CCU. Almost total camera parameter control is available, and having return video and tally operations as possibilities enhances communications.

However, multicore has its problems: The cables are thick, heavy and expensive; it takes forever to replace a connector since special tools are needed; the connectors are also a specialty item; the pins are easily bent; and any break in a conductor can cause not only intermittents but also total failure of the cable. The only solution when a cable fails is replacement of the whole, very costly unit.

Multicore cable connectors have given way to smaller, light cables. Triaxial cable, called triax, is now the standard for the OB industry, and it is finding its way into more and more industrial applications each day. It is used in the third illustration in Figure 9-6. Triax cable is like coax cable with a second dielectric (insulator) and a second shield (conductor) around the center conductor. The signal usually is digitized and multiplexed up and down the cable.

Advantages of triax are that the cable is lighter, cheaper and more rugged; the connector can be replaced in 30 minutes in the field; longer distances are possible because cables can be coupled and extended; and bulkhead and patch panels are easy to configure.

Longer transmission lengths (up to 10 miles) now utilize fiber cable (which also supports higher bandwidth HD signals).

Other display devices

The projection of video images is covered in other chapters in this book. However, the role of direct view monitors still is important for the foreseeable future. There are many aspects to consider when selecting a monitor for a given application, such as its functional role, whether color or monochrome is needed, and the image size of the display.

Presentation monitors can have a wide range of uses and can be found in a variety of locations, including corporate boardrooms, classrooms, trade shows and retail establishments. Their primary goal is the display of finished presentation material to viewers. The main difference between these monitors and our TV sets is that the monitors don't have a tuner to allow them to receive "off-air" broadcasts. Of course, the output of an external tuner can be fed to a monitor to give it the same capabilities.

The role of a monitor in production can be diverse. It can be used for source monitoring of inputs to a switcher or other devices to ascertain correct picture composition. It also can be used for program and preview monitoring of the output of a switcher, for on-air monitoring of the transmitted signal, and even for use in the field to monitor location recordings. Monitors used for these purposes typically are called production monitors.

The final broad category of monitors includes certain types of higher-grade monitors used exclusively for the technical monitoring of certain or all aspects of video signals. These monitors can determine if the correct color is present, and if the cameras or videotape recorders are set for or are producing the proper resolution, and are properly set up or registered. These monitors typically are called evaluation monitors.

Other types of monitoring devices that employ oscilloscope displays are available to examine the video signal. The two most common types of these devices are waveform monitors and vectorscopes.

Monitors work by employing decoding circuitry that takes the baseband composite signals and separates the chrominance from the luminance components. The signals then are routed to the gun(s) in the CRT, and the video signals voltage is converted to electron beams. The beams are directed to the correct phosphors on the inside front surface of the CRT by the shadow mask or aperture grill. This process is repeated 60 times each second.

Certain general specifications determine how well a monitor does at picture reproduction. These specs are, of course, dependent on the level of components in the unit itself. A monitor generally is judged by its resolving ability or resolution (expressed in number of lines horizontally), the screen size (usually measured diagonally), the raster's aspect ratio (4:3 for NTSC), the number of video and audio inputs, the image's brightness, and, in computer monitors, the image's contrast ratio, the pitch of the beam (determines resolution), and the pixel count.

Videotape machines

Videotape machines are called a number of different things—videotape recorders (VTRs), video-tape players and videocassette recorders (VCRs). All commercially available VTRs employ cassette mechanisms and technically are VCRs, but to most people that brings to mind a consumer machine. So we will refer generically to all videotape machines as VTRs. Videotape recorders and players fall into a number of categories:

> Low-end consumer units
> Mid-range industrial units
> High-end broadcast and production units

The use of videotape machines allows a number of functions. These include the "capture" of events from video cameras; time shifting of televised or broadcast events; archiving of events; multiple separate viewings; and incorporation of footage into other recordings.

Many recording modes are possible:

> Live on tape
> EFP—film-style
> Multiple/Multiple—multiple cameras into multiple VTRs

Selecting the right VTR

We want video recorders to capture the image as accurately as possible. There are many technical considerations to weigh when selecting the right videotape machine for a use or venue:

> Bandwidth range
> Signal-to-noise ratio
> Differential phase and gain
> Luminance/chrominance delay
> Dynamic tracking
> Controls
> Editing modes

Operational considerations need to be weighed as well:

> Powering
> Signal inputs and outputs
> Size and weight
> Ease of operation

And, of course, there is the all-important choice of a format. The recording format determines the quality level, and the application usually detemines the format. Many analog formats have been brought to market over the last 30-plus years, and a few still are available. They all differ considerably. The following table highlights a few video storage fromats for analog signals.

TABLE 9-1 Video formats for analog signals

FORMAT	APPLICATIONS	SIGNAL	PACKAGE	NOTES
2-inch Quad	High-end production	Analog composite	2 inch reel to reel	Rarely seen any more
OMEGA (Type C)	High-end production	Analog composite	1 inch reel to reel	No longer manufactured
BetaMax	Consumer	Analog composite	¹⁄₂ inch cassette	No longer manufactured
Video Home System (VHS)	Consumer applications	Analog composite	¹⁄₂ inch cassette	Inexpensive, but low quality recording 2-6 hour recording Widely used, so playback systems are easily found
Betacam	High-end production	Analog component	¹⁄₂ inch cassette	Expensive
Betacam SP	Broadcast station Independent productions Corporate video	Analog component	¹⁄₂ inch cassette	Expensive Over 400 lines of resolution
Super VHS (S-VHS)	Schools Small-market television newsrooms Low-end corporate editing suites	Analog component	¹⁄₂ inch cassette	400+ lines of resolution 2 hour recording Compatible editing equipment is inexpensive
Video8	Consumer	Analog composite	8mm cassette	
Video Hi-8	High-end consumer	Analog component	8mm cassette	

The need for digital formats

With analog VTR formats reaching their theoretical limit, product developers wanted to create formats that would produce multiple generations with no discernable degradation. The goal of all digital formats is to have a better signal than the previous analog signal while offering virtually indistinguishable copies.

However, the switch from analog to digital raises a number of questions. Among them:

How can we handle the conversion of analog to digital?
How is acquisition handled differently in digital?
How do we post to a digital format?
How are graphic elements and sound handled in a digital post environment?

Advances in digital technology have enhanced video recording. The greatest advantage of digital over analog is the high quality, multiple-generation capability of the digital VTR. Multiple generations do not have to deal with noise factors that plague analog systems. There is virtually no noise in the copying process. The generational quality is so good that we refer to it as a clone.

TABLE 9-2 Digital video formats and their uses

FORMAT	APPLICATIONS	SIGNAL	PACKAGE	NOTES
D-1	High-end graphics and production	Digital component	19mm cassette	4:2:2 sampling Sony proprietary format
D-2	Production in High-end broadcast (original digital workhorse format)	Digital Composite (4fsc)	19mm cassette (D1 cassette shell, different data format)	Marketed by Sony and Ampex (DCT)
D-3	High-end production	Digital composite	½ inch cassette	Digital replacement for analog format M-11 Panasonic proprietary format
Digital Betacam	High-end production	Digital component	½ inch cassette	Introduced as an alternative to D3 First format to offer "mild compression;" 2:2:1 bit-rate reduction Sony proprietary format
D-5	High-end production	Digital component	½ inch cassette	Looks like a VHS tape, but new formulation Designed as a lower cost alternative to D1 or Digital Betacam Panasonic proprietary format
Digital S (D-9)	Industrial/ broadcast production	Digital component	½ inch cassette	4:2:2 sampling (dual DV codecs) 720 pixels by 480 active lines 2 channels of audio MP tape optimization From JVC
DV	"Prosumer" market component	Digital	¼ inch 6.35 mm	4:1:1 sampling (intraframe DCT-based DV compression) 5:1 DV Compression 25 Mbps video data rate 1 or 2 audio channels 10 micron track pitch Many manufacturers

continued on next page

TABLE 9-2 Video formats for analog signals *(continued)*

FORMAT	APPLICATIONS	SIGNAL	PACKAGE	NOTES
DVCAM	Industrial production	Digital component	¹/₄ inch 6.35 mm	5:1 DV Compression 4:1:1 sampling 720 pixels by 480 active lines 2 or 4 audio tracks Inexpensive editing equipment 15 micron track pitch From Sony
DVCPRO	Professional	Digital component	¹/₄ inch 6.35 mm	4:1:1 sampling market 5:1 DV Compression 720 pixels by 480 active lines 2 channels of audio Inexpensive editing equipment From Panasonic
DVCPRO50	High-end production	Digital component	¹/₄ inch 6.35 mm	DV compression sampled at 4:2:2 Panasonic proprietary format
Betacam SX	Broadcast ENG	Digital component	¹/₂ inch cassette	4:2:2 sampling MPEG 2 Compression, Main profile at main level Sony proprietary format
MPEG-IMX	High-end production	Digital component	¹/₂ inch metal tape	4:2:2 sampling at 50Mbps MPEG 2 Compression (I-frame only) 4 or 8 channels of audio Sony proprietary format
HDCAM	High-end production Digital Cinema	Digital component	¹/₂ inch metal tape	9 17:6:6 sampling 1080i BRR compression Sony proprietary format
DVCPRO HD	High-end production Digital Cinema	Digital component	¹/₄ inch 6.35 mm	For 1080i or 720p acquisition Panasonic proprietary format
HDCAM SR	High-end production	Digital component	¹/₂ inch metal tape	4:2:2 or 4:4:4 sampling 12 channels of digital audio Sony proprietary format
Digital8	Consumer	Depends on implementation	8mm	Less expensive than DV Plays back 8mm andHi8
Hardrive	Consumer television recording Production acquisition (2003)	Depends on implementation	Computer drive	In 2003, acquisition formats debuted Random access to any part of the recording without having to wind through it
DVD (Digital Versatile Disc)	Used to store high quality video	Usually uses digital component	Optical disc	In 2003, acquisition formats debuted Random access—personalized menus allow access to different video clips Inexpensive

Shooting footage to facilitate editing

The goal of modern video editing is the communication of ideas and messages to a viewing audience by selecting shots, combining shots into sequences, and combining sequences into a program, then adding sound and graphics to complement and enhance the final program.

A number of styles of program creation are possible, depending on the method used in acquisition of the original footage. One of the most popular is called film-style. Segments are shot out of sequence, then edited together to create a cohesive product. The process of editing is analogous to film editing, but instead of moving physical stock (segments) of film, scenes stored on hard drives can be rearranged by moving segments on a graphic timeline. Video, audio, special effects, titles, graphics and other elements are combined to produce a finished "master."

Video editing

Traditionally video has been edited on linear, tape-based systems utilizing discrete components for machine control, video switching and audio mixing. This equipment is highly specialized, and varies broadly in price, depending on capabilities and technical specifications. These microprocessor-based editors are capable of orchestrating the efforts of numerous devices, including videotape machines (A/B roll), video switchers, audio mixers, digital video effects, character generators and so on.

Today's non-traditional systems are housed in or attached to a computer. Video and audio are stored on a hard disk inside the computer or on an array of external hard drives. This makes the system capable of instantaneous access to any video segment in a nonlinear fashion. The heart of the system, as with the older linear systems, is the software that acts as the controlling agent for all of the computer systems and attached video and audio peripherals.

In selecting an editing system, there are many criteria to keep in mind. The following questions need to be answered:

What is the technical level and expertise level of the operators and how many will have access to the system?

Is the background of the operators film or video?
What is the editing style of the editors?
Does the system have to be user friendly?

The shift to digital

As long as we are dealing with equivalent circuitry or devices, digital circuitry devices will give us better performance than comparable conventional analog circuitry devices. They produce other benefits as well, such as better picture matching with color cameras, and easier setup, operation and maintenance.

Digital also has certain inherent advantages. It requires no subcarrier; sampling reduces the analog waveform to digital "0s and 1s"; there is little degradation in subsequent generations; longer cable runs usually are possible; more capabilities are possible in digital circuitry; and some economies result from the reduction in scale.

A number of basic parameters determine how good the digitization will be.

The sampling rate: How often do we look at (or sample) the analog waveform?

The bit rate: How large is the sample? The larger, the better.

The bandwidth: What is the limiting bandwidth of the device or circuit?

The digital world

Many basic trends characterize the video industry today. Among them are the migration from analog to digital devices; the established movement toward nonlinear as opposed to linear editing systems; the emergence of the many DV compression tape and signal formats; and the planned transition from NTSC transmission to the DTV transmission scheme developed by the Advanced Television Standards Committee (ATSC). But the overriding element behind all of these trends is the digitization of just about everything involved in each trend.

Probably the last step in this trending process is the conversion from our current analog television broadcast transmission system to a digital one. The FCC created the ATSC in the fall of 1987 with a mandate to develop and/or investigate and then recommend a "scheme" for high definition television (HDTV) transmission for the United States. From 1988 until 1992 the ATSC investigated 23 different analog schemes. However, in 1990 General Instruments proposed a digital scheme that caught the committee's attention. The ATSC then abandoned all of the analog approaches; since the committee was political in nature and didn't wish to show too much favoritism, it formed the Grand Alliance in May of 1993. Three competing groups were told to come up with a suitable method for handling digital transmission of an advanced television signal.

Finally, on April 12, 1996, the FCC adopted the resulting rules for digital television transmission (DTV). However, instead of adopting one final scheme for handling digital high definition broadcasts, the commission adopted only a set of general technical guidelines that would allow for multiple types of signals (high definition and standard definition) within the same channel. This would allow a single HDTV transmission or multiple standard definition transmissions in the allotted bandwidth. But since the FCC didn't define what "high definition" was to be, multiple entities came up with differing types of high definition. Thus it might be possible to put a high-definition signal and one or two standard definition signals within the assigned frequency. There are aspects of the different DTV formats that appeal to the television, computer and film industries. There also is no agreement among the broadcast networks on any one universally accepted format.

On April 21, 1997, the FCC announced the channel allotments for future DTV transmissions. Broadcasters then proceeded to implement the schedule for going "on-the-air" with their DTV broadcasts within the specified timeline as established by the FCC. This required creating a separate plant within their existing operation—new transmitter, possibly a new tower, new antenna, new control room, etc. To demonstrate the need for such products, both 1080i and 720p equipment was displayed at the National Association of Broadcasters (NAB) show in April of 1998.

TABLE 9-3 The flavors of DTV

V lines	H pixels	Aspect Ratio	Frame Rates			
1080	1920	16:9	301		30P	24P
720	1280	16:9		60P	30P	24P
480	704	16:9	301	60P	30P	24P
480	704	4:3	301	60P	30P	24P
480	640	4:3	301	60P	30P	24P

The push to DTV

Viewers want sharper and clearer pictures on their TV sets with better, larger and wider (16x9 aspect ratio) displays. This is driven by consumer demand for a home cinema with surround sound and motion picture aspect ratios. Why else do consumers want DTV? Today's marketplace demands that everything be digital.

There are many features of the different DTV formats that appeal to television, computer and film people. To date there is no agreement among the networks on any one universally accepted format.

Digital transmission paths

The various digital signals discussed in this section need a means to travel from one place to another. Various methods have been approved by the different standardization organizations to accomplish this task. Do not confuse these "pipelines" with the signals that travel through them:

- **Uncompressed**
  SDI
  HD-SDI

- **Compressed**
  SDTI
      SMPTE standard
      Serial digital transport interface
      Elements of SDDI & QSDI
      270mbps pipeline
      Includes SDTI-CP (content package, which is a compressed MPEG-2 data stream up to 50Mbps)
  Firewire
      Apple created standard for linking digital camcorder to Mac
      Later approved by IEEE as standard 1394
  i-Link
      Name given to IEEE-1394 standard
      Newly adopted "standard"
          Sony has licensed 16 companies
          Matsushita, Adaptec, Fast, etc.
      DV 1/0 based on IEEE-1394
      Video/audio/subcode data
      Provides for control of decks through single cable from devices with circuitry.

10

TECHNICAL POWER

AND GROUND SYSTEMS

by **PHILIP GIDDINGS, PE**

Philip Giddings, PE, is the author of
*Audio Systems Design and
Installation,* and the founder of
Engineering Harmonics, Inc., an
international consulting and design
firm specializing in multimedia
systems. He can be contacted at
PGiddings@engineeringharmonics.com.

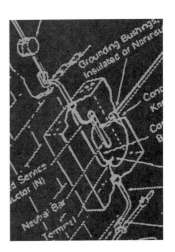

A necessary consideration in the design of audiovisual (AV) systems is how, specifically, the systems will be powered. AC power is the lifeblood of any electronic system, but it has the potential to be a source of difficulty. Poor power quality in an AV system can result in unreliable, unpredictable or generally unsatisfactory performance. What is worse, in many cases the fact that poor power quality is the cause of an AV system's lack of performance is not uncovered until extensive testing and debugging have been undertaken. As a result, it is prudent for the AV designer to give due consideration to power quality for an AV system.

AV, sound, video teleconferencing and other multimedia systems are generally referred to as technical systems in the context of larger capital projects such as, say, a commercial office tower or a university building. For this reason the term *technical power* often is used to describe the power that services these systems. Hence this chapter is about delivering appropriate technical power.

The chapter provides an introduction to the characteristics of power problems and to the tools for managing them. For more information see the references cited at the end of this section.

Power systems should be designed by an electrical engineer and installed by a licensed electrician due to life and equipment safety considerations. Electrical power has the ability to harm or kill people and damage equipment, by starting fires, for example. This is very different from AV systems for which few, if any, government regulations or codes specify system design and installation. There are no safety issues associated with AV systems. This chapter presumes that the appropriate experts will design the actual implementation and that the goal of readers here is to be able to make informed choices about the approach and options for power quality. This will allow them to have confidence at the outset that power-related deficiencies will not occur, or at least are unlikely. Further, as there are costs associated with each of the tools in the technical power palette, it is important to use the right ones and to be able to justify the relative expense of each.

Power system disturbances

A number of different types of disturbances can plague a power system. These, of course, are the reason that technical power systems are implemented. Disturbances can cause noise in analog circuits; a glitch in a computer system, causing it to falter or crash; reduced mean time between equipment failures; and permanent physical damage to the equipment power supply and associated electronics. Even the more minor effects can be completely unacceptable in certain environments and to certain users.

Disturbances in AC power circuits are a growing problem in AV facilities, due to the increased use of digital equipment and computerization. As more and more equipment becomes digital or computerized, the impact of glitches and crashes grows dramatically.

Most disturbances are not generated by the power utilities. A 1993 Florida power study reported the following sources for power disturbances:

- 60 percent from inside a facility, from office equipment, for example;
- 20 percent from neighbors;
- 15 percent from lighting; and
- 5 percent from the utility company.

Clearly, undertaking a local survey of the causes of potential disturbances is worthwhile as this could identify 80 percent of more of them.

In an existing facility it is possible to monitor the power with something as simple as an oscilloscope, or as specialized as a dedicated power-monitoring device. The specialized, purpose-built equipment will monitor all lines, the neutral and the ground, over a period of time and provide printed reports on the nature and frequency of disturbances. This allows for an appropriate solution to be retrofitted into a facility. Such equipment can be rented, or a power quality consulting service can be hired to provide this service and make recommendations.

Noise: Noise is a disturbance in the sinusoidal flow of electricity. It is referred to as electromagnetic interference (EMI) or radio frequency interference (RFI). Harmonics and transient impulses are another category of noise that causes distortion of the electrical voltage.

Sources of noise include electronic dimmers, poor electrical connections, switching power supplies, welders and motors. They may be nearby or some distance away. Where electrical lines run near radio frequency (RF) transmitters—television, radio, radar—the wires may conduct RFI into a building and the powered electronics.

Noise does not affect the ability of the power line to energize the equipment, but it can cause electronic equipment to perform poorly due to errors and glitches in programs or data.

Transient impulses. These are voltage fluctuations whose duration is much less than one AC cycle, generally in the range of less than one microsecond to several milliseconds. Transient impulses may be manifested as a single spike notch or damped oscillation. They may occur on a regular or an infrequent basis and may have a voltage of less than one volt up to many thousands of volts. These impulses and their potential for interference or equipment damage are determined by both the duration and the magnitude of the transient. The impulses can be either common or differential mode. Common mode impulses are those that occur simultaneously and are of equal magnitude on both sides of the line with respect to ground. They may be caused by lightning or power utility breakers momentarily tripping and re-closing. Differential mode impulses are those that occur between phase and ground and that therefore vary between phases. Generally they are caused by line-powered equipment that is inductive, or switched, or both. Examples of this would be switched air handling equipment or electronically controlled dimmed lighting. Often the frequency of the transients is a good indicator of their source. For example, a motor or electronic dimmer will have impulses hundreds of times per second, whereas a switched heavy air conditioning load may occur only when the equipment is cycled on or off a few times in the course of an hour.

Harmonics. Harmonics are periodic steady-state distortions of a sine wave due to equipment that generates frequencies at one or more multiples of 60Hz, such as 120Hz, 180 Hz and 240 Hz.

Electronic ballasts, variable speed drives and nonlinear switch-mode power supplies used in computers and many modern forms of electronics can cause harmonics. Switch mode power supplies draw current only in brief pulses at the top of each supply half cycle. They are a common source of harmonics in non-industrial environments.

Harmonics currents can cause overheating of electrical equipment and wiring, particularly neutrals conductors. Random breaker tripping also can occur.

The solutions to harmonics currents are specialized, and some are not part of standard power disturbance methodology. They include harmonics filters; increased neutral conductor size and upgraded wiring and grounding; isolation of nonlinear loads; special K-rated transformers; and other specialized techniques. A qualified electrical engineer or equivalent should administer these solutions. They are not discussed in detail in this chapter.

If it is expected that technical systems will have significant loads due to switching power supplies, then precautions should be taken to control neutral harmonics.

Undervoltages and overvoltages: These are any root mean square (RMS) voltage fluctuations that are greater than approximately 10 percent of the line voltage and that last more than 2.5 seconds. Undervoltage conditions of 5 percent or more are often caused purposely by the power utility company during periods of high usage, such as hot weather periods when air conditioning loads are high. These "brownouts" help to extend the power system's capability. Overvoltage conditions can occur if the power utility company is having difficulty with regulation, or if unexpectedly light power loads occur, as when an accident such as a fire or explosion results in power being disconnected from a city block.

Sags and surges: These are any voltage fluctuations that are greater than approximately 10 percent of the line voltage and that last more than half of an AC cycle (8 milliseconds) and less than 2.5 seconds. Switching on heavy loads that have very high inrush currents during their startup often causes sags. Surges may occur when large inductive loads are removed from a line.

Dropouts: Dropouts occur whenever the voltage drops to zero for any period greater than a portion of an AC cycle. Dropouts may be caused by faults that occur and then are quickly cleared from the line by protected devices such as circuit breakers.

Outages: Also called line interruptions, these are dropouts that persist. They may be caused by excessive demands on the power system, accidental damage to power lines or lightning strikes.

Frequency variations: Changes in power line frequency (60Hz in North America) are very rare in modern power systems that are part of a grid. However if locally generated power is available and is not connected to the power grid, variations may occur and can be as high as 10Hz.

Technical power

A technical power system is one put in place to provide power to technical equipment or systems such as AV, video teleconferencing or broadcast. We have seen that power systems may suffer from a wide variety of disturbances that can affect the operation of a technical system. This section describes the various tools and techniques that can be applied to ensure power quality.

Power conditioning: Power conditioning units can be added to a power distribution system to improve its power quality. This can be done at the design stage, before a power system is installed, or after the fact when power quality problems are found to be plaguing a technical systems operation. The numerous devices described below address power quality issues.

Transient voltage surge suppression (TVSS). This is a system of line filters, and it is among the simplest and least costly forms of power conditioning. The effectiveness of TVSS units varies greatly, however, and the cheaper units have given these devices a bad reputation that is quite underserved by the better units. TVSS filters are intended only to deal with transient disturbances and, if so used, can be effective against most or all combinations of common and differential-mode disturbances. In this way they may have an advantage over a shielded isolation transformer (see below), which exhibits its best attenuation with common-mode signals and not differential-mode types. Their effectiveness diminishes as the frequency of the disturbances decreases, and care must be taken in interpreting the specifications.

Many filters use metal oxide varistors (MOVs) as their primary means of defense. MOVs reduce their resistance in the presence of a high voltage and can be used to shunt transient voltages either across phase and neutral or to ground. The concern with MOVs is that these devices are sacrificial and tend to blow open or short after a number or uses or after an extreme surge. As a result they require a regular maintenance program. A method to test that the devices are still operational is available on some models and is a great benefit.

The most effective line filters use inductors mounted in series with the power lines. One such product is called Surgex. These units deliver outstanding performance, suppressing all surge modes, and they have no sacrificial parts. The units generally are used at the point of supply.

While use of TVSS at the point of supply is the first line of defense, a comprehensive TVSS design, as recommended by many manufacturers, will provide surge suppressors at the service entrance, at panelboards and at the point of supply.

It should be noted that TVSS should also be provided to incoming telephone, cable and modem lines as these can provide a back door entrance for lightning and other surges.

Isolation transformer. The term *isolation transformer* is often used loosely. Transformers have DC isolation between the primary and secondary windings and therefore can be considered isolation transformers. Only specially designed units provide high isolation as frequency increases, and these are referred to as shielded units or Faraday shielded units.

Faraday shielded isolation transformers are effective in attenuating common-mode impulses and are not intended to deal with differential-mode (normal-mode) impulses, which they attenuate, to varying degrees, less well. They commonly are used in technical power systems and are discussed further below.

Electrical signals are passed through a transformer in two ways. The way the transformer is intended to operate is through the inductive coupling of the primary and secondary windings, and this mode predominates at lower frequencies where the transformer is intended to operate. Differential signals are passed through the transformer in this way; a current in one winding induces a current in the other winding due to their mutual inductance. A second mode of passing an electrical signal through a transformer is via the capacitive coupling between the windings. This increases with frequency and often becomes significant well beyond the normal operating range of the unit. Common-mode noise can be transmitted in this way. This is an undesirable side effect of most transformers. It is eliminated through the use of electric field shields, commonly referred to as Faraday shields, between the windings to reduce the capacitive coupling.

A standard transformer, such as that used by the power utility company, has a large coupling capacitance between the primary and secondary windings, causing transients to be transmitted across windings. A Faraday shielded isolation transformer reduces the coupling capacitance (to around 0.001pF) and hence the transmitted common-mode transients. Further reduction in the coupling capacitance (to as low as 0.0005pF) is obtained in quality units with the use of box electrostatic shields around the primary and secondary windings. Varying degrees and numbers of these shields are available. The differential-mode attenuation of the transformer typically begins at the point a little below 1kHz where many of the DC power supplies, typical of many computers and analog devices, begin to drop in performance, with the overall result of good broadband performance. A minimum performance specification for isolation of an isolation transformer is 20dB above 2kHz.

Isolation transformers attenuate only transient and high frequency disturbances. If undervoltages and overvoltages, sags, surges and dropouts are expected, other conditioning is preferred. Conditioning that will provide the benefits of an isolation transformer usually can be selected.

The impedance to earth of the ground connection will determine in part the effectiveness of a Faraday shield.

Line voltage regulator. Line voltage regulators provide protection from moderate line overvoltages and undervoltages as well as sags and surges. There are many different types, which vary in response time, efficiency at different loads, output impedance, audible noise level and the range of input voltages for constant output voltage. They vary also in the amount of attenuation of impulses provided, with autotransformer types providing almost none. These units could, for example, be used where the power is clean but summer brownouts due to air-conditioner loads cause computer failures.

The basic types of line voltage regulators are: the motor-driven autotransformer with series transformer; the motor-driven induction regulator; the saturable reactor; the electronic tap-switching autotransformer; and the ferroresonant transformer. The motor-driven types are low-cost and handle heavy loads, although their slow response corrects only gradual changes. The brushes in these units normally will track back and forth on an almost continuous basis over a small number of windings and will require regular maintenance. Motor-driven units have been used for large touring sound systems, which, together with lighting equipment, often tax the local supply. If this arrangement is used with an isolation transformer or filter, some line conditioning is provided. The low cost to upgrade such a unit to an improved ferroresonant transformer, which also provides filtering, makes this alternative attractive.

Line conditioner. Line conditioners provide protection from both voltage variations and transients, leaving only dropouts and interruptions as potential problems. They may combine the features of TVSS, an isolation transformer and a voltage regulator into one operational unit that is less costly then the sum of the three. Line conditioners are popular wherever computers are in use and where loss of data during power outages is not critical.

Uninterruptible power supply. An uninterruptible power supply is usually the most expensive alternative for power conditioning. It contains chargers, battery banks and inverters allowing the incoming power to shut off completely while power to the load is maintained until the batteries die. Preferred units are constantly online and are switched out of the circuit only for service or when there is an internal failure. Other units are normally offline and are switched on during a power failure. The former is preferred because it provides excellent full-time protection from transients and from short and long- term voltage variations. These units are the preferred choice for computerized systems in which crashes and reboot time delays are unacceptable.

Power distribution: Because many power disturbances are generated within a facility, a good line of defense is to provide separate and dedicated power distribution for the technical systems. This approach has always been commonplace in broadcast facilities and is no longer uncommon in modern office buildings, where PCs often have their own dedicated panelboards and isolated ground branch circuits.

In a new facility, providing dedicated power distribution for technical equipment is a worthwhile approach that is not very costly given that some form of power distribution must be provided regardless. The larger the AV facility, the smaller the incremental cost of a dedicated system.

When dedicated power distribution is implemented, the effects of power disturbances from within the building can be eliminated. This can be much less costly then providing extensive power conditioning equipment.

A comprehensive technical power distribution system starts at the service entrance of the building and extends to any and all powered technical equipment. The power is distributed in a star type topology as shown in Figure 10-1. This figure also shows the distribution of an isolated ground as dashed lines; these lines will be referred to in a later section called Isolated Ground. Note that a technical power system is not necessarily accompanied by an isolated ground system.

Service entrance. The technical facility, whether it has one room or many, should derive all its power from one central location that is, ideally, in the service entrance of the building. This is usually the location of the cleanest power. Ideally the power is derived directly from its own transformer (T-A in Figure 10-1), preferably a shielded isolation type.

The Main Technical Distribution Panel (TP-A0 in the figure) in the service entrance will distribute the power (and the isolated ground, if required) to all other locations within the facility via feeders to subpanels. In a very small installation it may power branch circuits directly, without feeders or subpanels.

Panels, feeders and subpanels. The subpanels (panelboards) are located within 100 feet of the technical equipment. More panels are used if necessary to achieve this. Where the AV equipment loads are substantial, a greater density of panels is needed. They are fed via feeders from the Main Technical Distribution Panelboard. In a presentation theater or training facility, for example, the subpanels often are located in or near a control room or equipment closet.

The panelboards should not be adjacent to the main technical signal wire or equipment centers of the facility. The AC currents involved could create sufficient electromagnetic fields to induce hum in nearby circuits. If the power is completely contained in electrical metal tubing (EMT) or rigid conduit, the fields will be reduced but not eliminated. A separation of 5' or 10' (1.6m or 3.1 m) is acceptable for a 50-amp panelboard in a steel chassis and raceway when microphone signals are present. These data are based on practical experience.

In a large complex, panels may be in an equipment or utility room and power feeders that in turn power subpanels.

Branch circuits and outlets. From the subpanels (panelboards), the branch circuits will run to the various electronics, racks, communications equipment and wall outlets, for example.

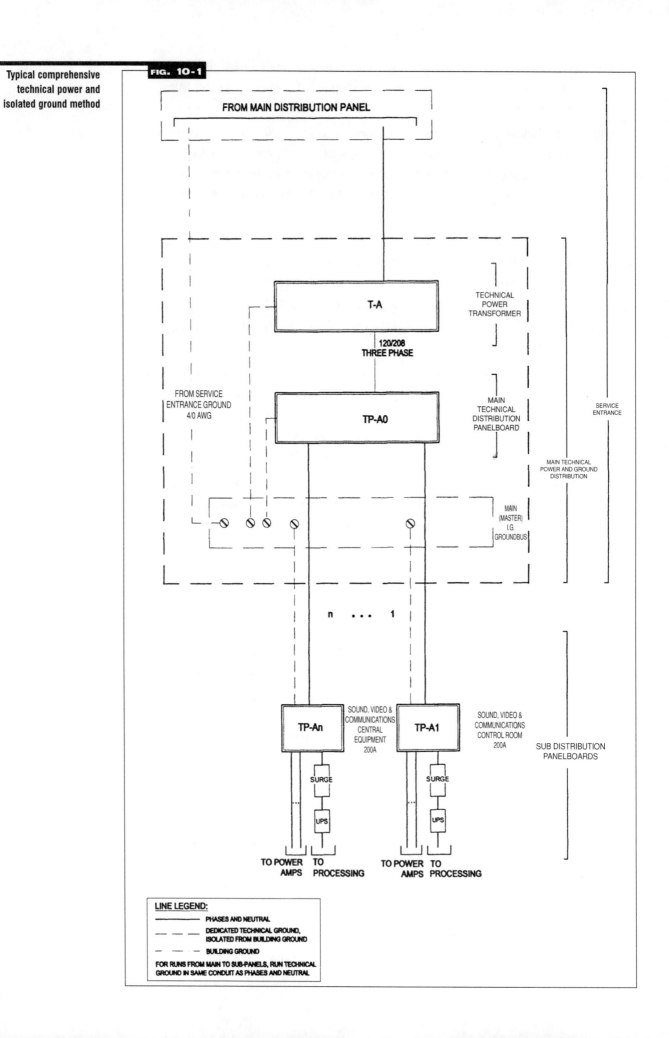

Typical comprehensive technical power and isolated ground method

FIG. 10-1

FROM MAIN DISTRIBUTION PANEL

T-A

TECHNICAL POWER TRANSFORMER

120/208 THREE PHASE

TP-A0

MAIN TECHNICAL DISTRIBUTION PANELBOARD

FROM SERVICE ENTRANCE GROUND 4/0 AWG

SERVICE ENTRANCE

MAIN TECHNICAL POWER AND GROUND DISTRIBUTION

MAIN (MASTER) I.G. GROUNDBUS

n . . . 1

TP-An

SOUND, VIDEO & COMMUNICATIONS CENTRAL EQUIPMENT 200A

TP-A1

SOUND, VIDEO & COMMUNICATIONS CONTROL ROOM 200A

SUB DISTRIBUTION PANELBOARDS

SURGE

UPS

SURGE

UPS

TO POWER AMPS

TO PROCESSING

TO POWER AMPS

TO PROCESSING

LINE LEGEND:

——————— PHASES AND NEUTRAL

– – – – – DEDICATED TECHNICAL GROUND, ISOLATED FROM BUILDING GROUND

— - — - BUILDING GROUND

FOR RUNS FROM MAIN TO SUB-PANELS, RUN TECHNICAL GROUND IN SAME CONDUIT AS PHASES AND NEUTRAL

These branch circuits must be used only for the technical equipment. If they power other equipment such as soft drink and coffee machines, vacuum cleaners and heaters, EMI may be introduced into the power and ground system. Where the branch circuits run into equipment racks or rooms, maintaining control is easy. Circuits that are accessible to users and staff should be identified with a label saying the equivalent of "FOR AV EQUIPMENT ONLY."

About power systems grounding. For AV systems designers, grounding is not a new idea. However, when it is used to describe power systems, grounding means something different from the grounding used in AV systems. In accordance with industry practice, a grounded power system is one that makes use of both system grounding and equipment grounding. Each of these has a distinct purpose and implementation. What they are and how they differ will be explained in the following two sections.

Grounding methods are often reviewed and modified in light of AV system operational irregularities, and unsafe, ineffective solutions often result. Knowledge of the power systems grounding, as it relates to the ground needed for AV equipment to operate correctly, is important. Isolated grounding and how it can be incorporated into a system with equipment and system grounding is discussed later in a section called "Isolated Ground."

Safety, reliability and cost savings are the benefits of system and equipment grounding. These grounding methods are used in most urban areas of North America, Great Britain, Europe and Australia. Generally anywhere three contact power connectors are used, an implementation with system and equipment grounding is in place.

Power grounding methods are used by power utility companies and electricians in their installations of power distribution systems. These techniques are covered in documents published by most governments, often at the federal level. They are required practice if approval of the power system is to be granted by the authorities. If a system is not "code worthy" and a fault resulting in property damage or personal injury is traced back to improper methods or practice, as documented in the code, then the installer or system designer is clearly at fault and may be liable. In some cases local or regional authorities modify these requirements. Examples of these documents are given in Table 10-1. The governing standards should be a part of every AV system designer's library.

TABLE 10-1 Some power codes and regulations

COUNTRY	REGULATIONS
United States	United States National Electrical Code@ (NEC)®, published by the National Fire Prevention Association (NFPA), Quincy, Mass.
Canada	Canadian Electrical Code (CEC), published by the Canadian Standards Association (CSA), Rexdale, Ontario.
England	Wiring Regulations, often called the "IEE Regs," produced by the Institute of Electrical Engineers. See also the British Standards Institute (BSI) publications and contact the Electricity Council or the Central Electricity Generating Board, London.
Australia	Electrical Installation: Buildings, Structures and Premises, commonly referred to as the "SAA Wiring Rules," published by Standards Association of Australia, North Sydney.

The National Electrical Code is copyright© 2002, National Fire Protection Association. National Electrical Code© and NEC® are Registered Trademarks of the National Fire Prevention Association, Inc., Quincy, Mass. The Canadian Electrical Code is copyright© 1998, Canadian Standards Association.

■ **System grounding**—System grounding is defined in the Institute of Electrical and Electronics Engineers, Inc. (IEEE) standard dictionary (STD 100-1984) as "connections to earth of any conductors in an electrical transmission system that carry current in normal operation." It often is referred to as circuit grounding, a more descriptive term. Power transmission systems in urban areas generally make use of system grounding by means of a grounded neutral.

System grounding requires electrically connecting one side of the AC power circuit to the ground by physically running a conductor into the earth. This may be done at the generator or transformer source and then again at the distribution points, including the service entrance of a building. It is illustrated in Figure 10-2. System grounding is demonstrated by the electrical connection to the cold water pipe or ground rod system or both. Because of this connection the neutral contact of an electrical power outlet is a short to ground (earth) and consequently also to the equipment ground contact and structural building steel.

Essential elements of technical equipment and system grounding

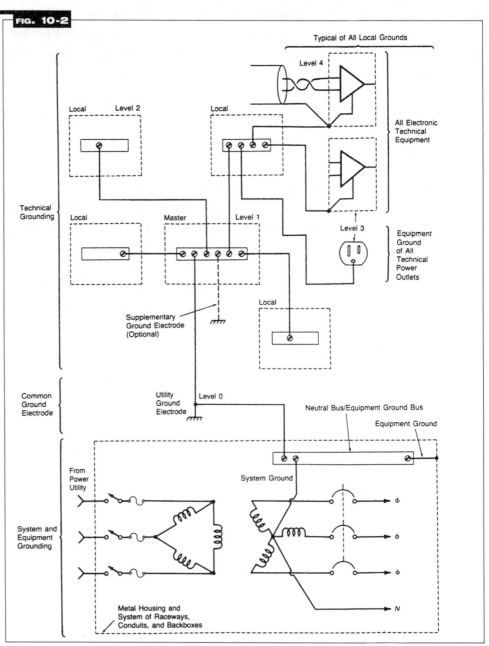

■ **Equipment grounding**—Equipment grounding is defined in the IEEE standard dictionary (STD 100-1984) as "connections to earth from one or more of non-current-carrying metal parts of the wiring system or of apparatus connected to the system." Equipment that may be grounded includes metal parts such as metal conduits, raceways, outlet boxes, cabinets and enclosures. These conductive elements do not carry current under normal operation. It is only in the event of a fault where a live wire contacts them that short-circuit current is carried. The equipment ground system or conductors are commonly referred to by the layperson as the safety ground, although other terms include the building electrical ground and the U-ground. (The term *U-ground* comes from the shape of the ground contact on an AC plug in North America.) Figure 10-3 illustrates the many locations where equipment grounding takes place.

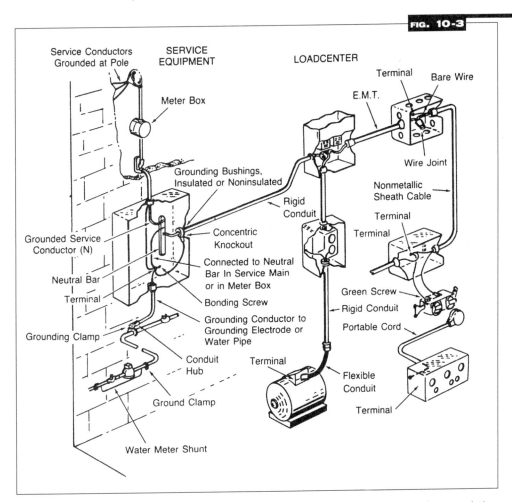

FIG. 10-3

Equipment grounding

In addition to the electrical code requirements of many countries, employee safety regulations state that equipment grounding is mandatory in most industrial and commercial situations. Countries that have not incorporated a third ground wire on plug-in equipment are not fully utilizing the safety potential available.

The main benefits of these wires and connections are twofold:

■ If all equipment housings are grounded or, in other words, bonded together electrically, then it is not possible to have potential differences among equipment even under fault conditions. In addition, if the equipment ground is connected to the structural steel, then the building structure and equipment must also remain at similar potentials under fault conditions. This means, for example, that if a person touches two pieces of equipment, one of which has a short to ground internally and is creating a voltage on the ground, that person will be exposed to a minimal potential difference, as the non-faulty piece of equipment is also at a raised ground potential. A grounded equipment chassis also minimizes the voltage potential to a person holding a faulty electric tool while standing on a steel or wet concrete floor.

- Equipment grounds, while attempting to keep everything at the same potential (that is, ground), also provide a low-impedance connection to ground for the fault current, and in this way ensure that the short-circuit current will be high and that a circuit protection device will blow quickly, removing any hazard. For this to be true, a grounded neutral must also be in place.

Equipment grounding is physically separate from system grounding, although since both are ground they obviously have a common point of connection—the earth. In buildings, this joining of the systems to ground occurs at the building service equipment.

In addition to the safety benefit, equipment grounding of chassis reduces the electromagnetic interference (EMI) radiated from a "noisy" piece of equipment, such as a motor, and reduces that picked up by a grounded piece of electronic equipment.

Isolated ground

Isolated ground (I.G.) techniques have evolved with the goal of minimizing noise input to the technical system under all conditions of operation and interconnection. Isolated grounds are not part of most power quality programs and are not intended to reduce power disturbances, although they also help with this. I.G. systems are intended to provide a stable and quiet electrical ground reference to pieces of equipment and their audio and video circuits. This keeps analog circuits quiet and digital circuits stable by maintaining a common ground refer- ence, and leads to the ultimate goal and benefit of the highest possible AV reliability and quality of service.

In their simplest, and in fact most common form, isolated ground systems consist of insu- lated ground wires from the panelboard to the isolated ground AC power outlets. This system is commonly used in many office environments for the power to PCs. It is shown in Figure 10-4, and is discussed in the National Electrical Code (NEC) section 250-74. The basic approach is adequate for most AV systems, particularly where all parts are powered from the same panelboard.

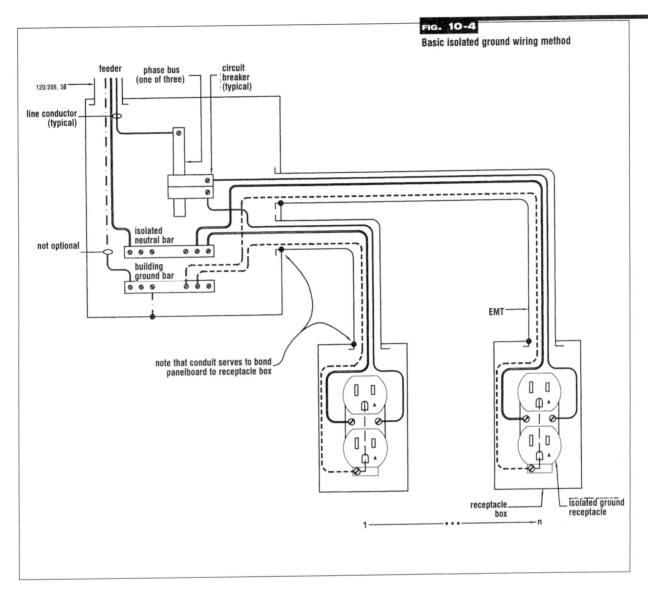

FIG. 10-4

Basic isolated ground wiring method

feeder

phase bus
(one of three)

circuit
breaker
(typical)

120/208, 3∅

line conductor
(typical)

not optional

isolated
neutral bar

building
ground bar

note that conduit serves to bond
panelboard to receptacle box

EMT

receptacle
box

isolated ground
receptacle

1 — • • • — n

The isolated star technical ground system: When AV systems become extensive and spread over a number of rooms, such as in a training facility, more then one panelboard is necessary. If there is considerable signal connectivity between the rooms and they are powered from different panelboards, the isolated ground is best carried between panels to maintain a constant ground reference. Implementing this requirement results in considerably more complexity. This section identifies the measures that must be taken.

The isolated star system provides an approach to grounding that has a minimum of technical compromises and meets the requirements of equipment grounding, while being relatively practical to install, troubleshoot and maintain. A large isolated ground system always will be accompanied by the technical power distribution of subpanels as described earlier, so adding isolated ground simply adds to that system. Chart 10-1 illustrates the star system's several levels of ground reference. These are shown in the top half of Figure 10-2. Note that the terminology used here does not represent an industry standard but is being suggested and used to develop the ideas.

CHART 10-1 The isolated star ground levels (suggested)

Level 0	The ground electrode provides the connection to earth for the entire system of conductors and buses.
Level 1	The master technical (I.G.) ground reference bus is the central hub for all technical ground conductors. There is only one in any facility. This point connects to the "technical" ground electrode system, the building power electrode system and the building equipment ground system as well as the neutral conductor for the power distribution.
Level 2	The local (or area) technical ground reference busses are connected to the master ground reference by heavy conductors. There can be one or many of these, depending on the size of the facility. They may be located near a studio/control room, a machine room, a remote amplifier rack or a mobile truck location, for example. Where these areas are close together a single bus services them.
Level 3	The equipment technical ground reference is the reference in each piece of electronics or passive device, such as a jackfield, provided by conductors from the local reference. There is one conductor for each piece of equipment, so there are many of these. On many occasions an entire rack or subassembly is treated as a single piece of equipment in which all equipment grounds are bonded together and then connected to the local ground bus over a single connector.
Level 4	The circuit and shield ground reference is provided by each piece of equipment to the circuits, interconnecting wiring and shields with which it interfaces.

In a small system there may be one less level; level 1 and 2 may be combined.

The entire technical ground system of conductors and ground busses is insulated and isolated from all other systems. At the master technical ground reference bus a connection is made to the ground electrode system, the system ground and the equipment ground. This is illustrated in Figure 10-2. It gives all of the ground systems a single and definite common ground point, making them effectively bonded together. In addition, a supplementary ground electrode (earth connection) may be connected at this point, if so desired.

There are four key points that must be appreciated to understand why this system works and should be used:

- **Equipment within a given area has individual conductors providing a reference.** This means that common-impedance coupling is eliminated between pieces of equipment in a given area. The equipment is likely to have many signal interconnections and hence is most prone to this type of noise coupling. For example, if one piece of equipment has a "leaky" power supply or strong coupling to some other noise influence that creates a ground current, the resulting error in the ground reference will have minimal effects on other pieces of equipment in that area.

- **Equipment within a given area has a ground reference to the same "level."** This means that pieces of equipment in a given area that may have many interconnections will have similar references since they are connected to the same point. In other words, they have been bonded together and thus have a low-impedance connection to each other. Therefore they are likely to have similar ground reference, even if it is not at earth (reference) potential.

- **Each piece of equipment has only one possible path to ground.** This means that there cannot be any ground loops.

- **Each piece of equipment has a similar resistance to ground.** This means that, assuming leakage currents into the ground at each node are similar, the potential above ground of each node is the same, so that the equipment will maintain similar ground references.

The star technical ground system is also the equipment ground for the equipment connected to it. It is important to realize, however, that the grounding system created for any technical system consists of two equipment grounds. These are the insulated technical ground and the traditional uninsulated equipment ground for grounding conduits, raceways and back boxes. Because the technical ground is intentionally isolated from raceways and so on, the traditional equipment ground is required for this purpose. In a non-technical system a single equipment ground is used for equipment, conduits, raceways and back boxes.

In other words, an isolated ground power outlet in a wall-mounted box has the ground terminal connected to the technical ground, while the box in which it is mounted must be grounded with an equipment ground conductor. (This, of course, is why an isolated outlet is used— to insulate these two systems from each other.)

Distribution: The technical ground is distributed in a star configuration like the technical power, making it easy to lay out so that the master and local ground busses are located with the distribution panelboards. The isolated ground is isolated from all others, except at the electrical connection where the master technical ground connects to the neutral bus, equipment bonding jumper and ground electrode system at the service equipment location as shown in Figure 10-2.

Figure 10-1 shows the central ground bus in the main technical power and ground distribution and how the grounds are distributed to the panels from this point.

Panelboards and subpanels. Typical panelboard wiring is shown in Figure 10-5. Associated with each distribution panelboard or subpanel will be a box containing the isolated ground bus.

The size and number of technical/safety ground conductors at each location make a separate box necessary, although it should be verified that a separate box would obtain approval from the inspecting authority. Inspectors may insist that these connections occur inside the distribution panel. This box can be clearly labeled "Isolated / Technical Ground" so that it is given due respect in the event of changes or additions. Using a separate box also means that during system verification it is possible to isolate ground wires for test purposes without opening power distribution panelboards; this is a distinct safety feature. It also allows terminals to be tightened easily and safely during routine maintenance. This additional "equipment ground bus," as it is called in the National Electrical Code, is the local technical ground bus or reference point. The ground network may, in this way, form the same star networks as the power system.

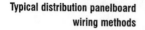

Typical distribution panelboard wiring methods

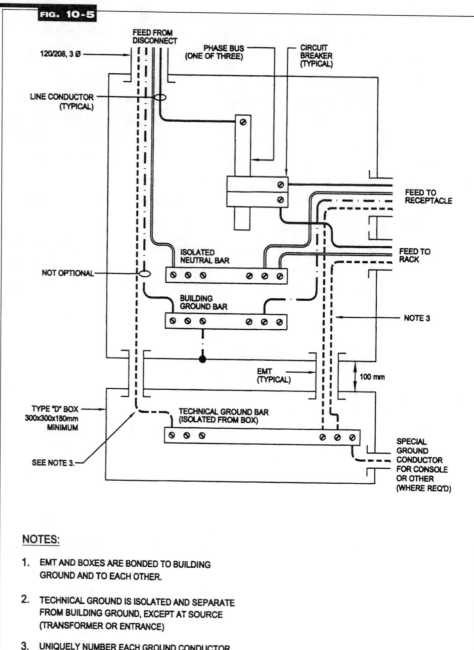

FIG. 10-5

NOTES:

1. EMT AND BOXES ARE BONDED TO BUILDING GROUND AND TO EACH OTHER.

2. TECHNICAL GROUND IS ISOLATED AND SEPARATE FROM BUILDING GROUND, EXCEPT AT SOURCE (TRANSFORMER OR ENTRANCE)

3. UNIQUELY NUMBER EACH GROUND CONDUCTOR AT BOTH ENDS.

Branch circuits and outlets. Typical outlet wiring is shown in Figure 10-6. From the panelboards (or subpanels, if they exist) will run the branch circuits (normally 15A in North America) to the various electronics and signal processing racks, communications equipment and wall outlets, for example. Each branch circuit may have several insulated ground wires run with it, ideally one for each outlet to be powered, as well as an uninsulated equipment ground wire for the purpose of equipment grounding the back boxes. When conduit is used, this often serves as the equipment grounding conductor and the uninsulated conductor is omitted.

FIG. 10-6   **Typical duplex outlet wiring methods**

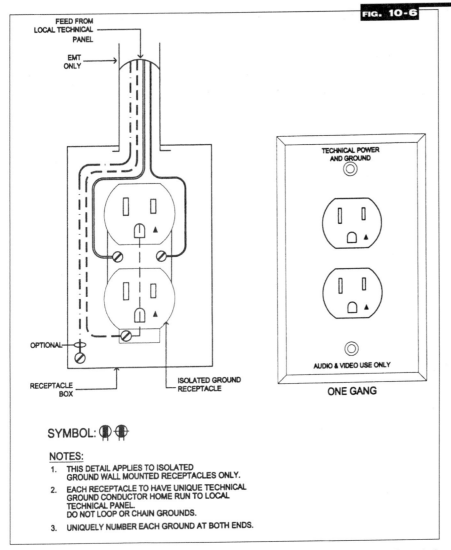

FEED FROM
LOCAL TECHNICAL
PANEL

EMT
ONLY

OPTIONAL

RECEPTACLE
BOX

ISOLATED GROUND
RECEPTACLE

TECHNICAL POWER
AND GROUND

AUDIO & VIDEO USE ONLY

ONE GANG

SYMBOL:

NOTES:
1. THIS DETAIL APPLIES TO ISOLATED
    GROUND WALL MOUNTED RECEPTACLES ONLY.
2. EACH RECEPTACLE TO HAVE UNIQUE TECHNICAL
    GROUND CONDUCTOR HOME RUN TO LOCAL
    TECHNICAL PANEL.
    DO NOT LOOP OR CHAIN GROUNDS.
3. UNIQUELY NUMBER EACH GROUND AT BOTH ENDS.

The routing of branch circuits should be kept away from AV and other signal-level circuits. Where AV and power cable conduits run parallel they should be spaced apart, at least 6" (0.15 m) for runs up to 15' (4.7 m), and 24" (0.61 m) or more for longer runs. Where non-metallic conduit (PVC) is used, these distances should be increased by a factor of four or more, and if possible power lines should be twisted pairs of line and neutral. If power and AV circuits must cross, whether in conduit or not, they should do so at 90 degrees to minimize the magnetic coupling.

In North America, several types of high-quality isolated ground outlets include the Hubbel IG 5262, the General Electric GE 8000IG and the Daniel Woodhead 5262DWIG. Isolated ground outlets normally are orange (or salmon) colored or have a triangle symbol on the front face identifying them. They generally are of high quality (hospital grade), and this ensures a good electrical connection between the technical ground conductor and the ground pin on the equipment plug. Economy outlets can lose their spring tension and hence their ground connection integrity. Hospital grade outlets often are identified with a green circular dot.

The box that mounts an isolated outlet is grounded through the conduit, armored cable and/or uninsulated equipment grounding conductor to the panelboard and eventually to earth. It does so in an uncontrolled and potentially multipath manner in buildings of steel construction, due to the many possible ground paths.

Racks. Where racks of equipment are used it is common to bring all the technical grounds from the equipment to a bus in the rack and to run a single wire from this to the local bus. This is illustrated in Figure 10-7. Only one wire is brought back from each group of racks. This obviously simplifies wiring and serves to bond the equipment in the rack effectively. In practice, it is satisfactory. It is suggested that groups of racks ideally would contain equipment of one type, such as all microphone level, all line level or all computer hardware so that the differing systems do not share a ground wire.

This approach creates ground loops within the rack. These loops exist due to multiple paths to ground as follows. The chassis of the equipment usually is in electrical contact in the rack, and the circuit reference is grounded to the rack via the technical ground wires to the rack ground bus. Another ground loop also exists between any two pieces of equipment that have their chassis in electrical contact with the rack frame. Being within the rack, these ground loops are physically small and typically not subject to strong fields or ground potential differences, so that they rarely introduce noise into the system—particularly where all equipment is balanced and low impedance.

Typical rack wiring methods

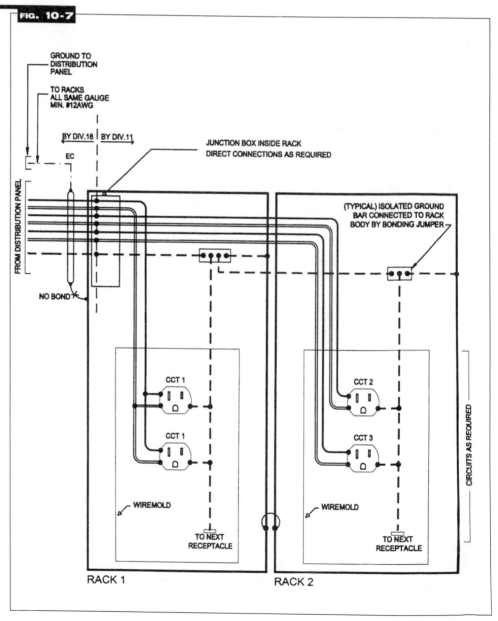

Figure 10-8 shows other considerations for physically installing racks in a manner that accommodates an isolated ground.

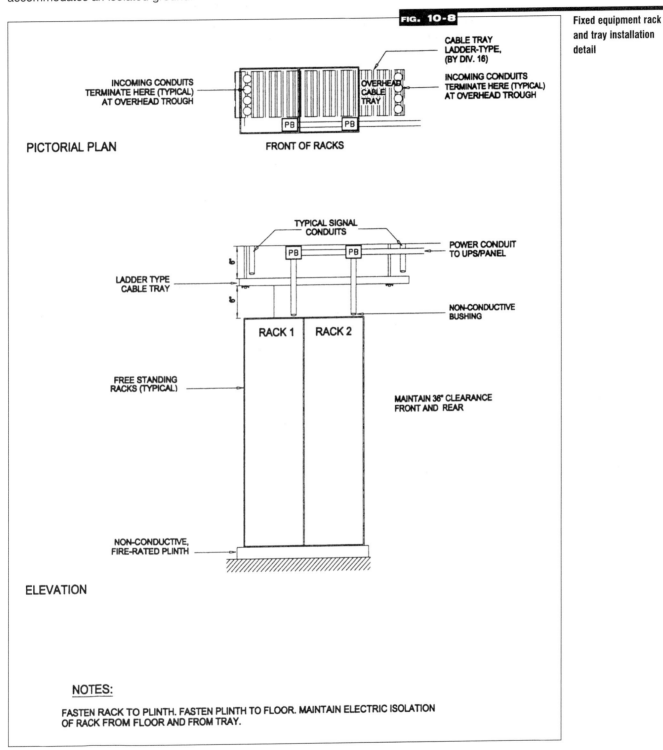

FIG. 10-8

PICTORIAL PLAN

CABLE TRAY LADDER-TYPE, (BY DIV. 16)

INCOMING CONDUITS TERMINATE HERE (TYPICAL) AT OVERHEAD TROUGH

OVERHEAD CABLE TRAY

INCOMING CONDUITS TERMINATE HERE (TYPICAL) AT OVERHEAD TROUGH

FRONT OF RACKS

TYPICAL SIGNAL CONDUITS

POWER CONDUIT TO UPS/PANEL

LADDER TYPE CABLE TRAY

NON-CONDUCTIVE BUSHING

RACK 1   RACK 2

FREE STANDING RACKS (TYPICAL)

MAINTAIN 36" CLEARANCE FRONT AND REAR

NON-CONDUCTIVE, FIRE-RATED PLINTH

ELEVATION

NOTES:

FASTEN RACK TO PLINTH. FASTEN PLINTH TO FLOOR. MAINTAIN ELECTRIC ISOLATION OF RACK FROM FLOOR AND FROM TRAY.

Earth Connection: It should be noted that a good connection to earth is important in dissipating stray RFI currents and energy due to lighting strikes. Establishing a low resistance earth connection can be difficult in dry or rocky terrain. Companies such as Lyncole XIT provide specialized rods for low resistance requirements.

References

Giddings P. 1990. *Audio Systems Design and Installation.* Boston: Focal Press.

Giddings P. *Getting a Perspective on Noise in Audio Systems.*
http://www.engineeringharmonics.com/papers/8.html.

Bibliography

Burdick, A.H. 1986. *A Clean Audio Installation Guide.* North Syracuse, N.Y.: Benchmark Media Systems, Inc.

Davis, C., and D. Davis. Grounding and Shielding Workshop. *Tech Topics.* 12: 10 (1985).

Giddings, P. An Introduction to Electromagnetic Compatibility (EMC) and Electromagnetic Interference (EMI) for Audio Systems Designers. *J. Audio Eng. Soc.* 37: 570—585 (1989 July/Aug.).

Macatee, S.R. Considerations in Grounding and Shielding Audio Devices. *J. Audio Eng. Soc. (Engineering Reports).* 43: 472—483 (1995 June).

Morrison, R. 1977. *Grounding and Shielding Techniques in Instrumentation,* 2nd ed. New York: Wiley Interscience.

Morrison, R., and W. H. Lewis. 1990. *Grounding and Shielding in Facilities.* New York: Wiley Interscience.

Muncy, N.A. Noise Susceptibility in Analog and Digital Signal Processing Systems. *J. Audio Eng. Soc.* 43: 435—453 (1995 June).

Perkins C. Automated Test and Measurement of Common Impedance Coupling in Audio System Shield Terminations. *J. Audio Eng. Soc. (Engineering Reports).* 43: 488—497 (1995 June).

Violette, N., and D. White. 1987. *Electromagnetic Compatibility Handbook.* New York: Van Nostrand Reinhold.

Whitlock, B. Balanced Lines in Audio Systems: Fact, Fiction, and Transformers. *J. Audio Eng. Soc.* 43: 454—464 (1995 June).

Windt, J. An Easily Implemented Procedure for Identifying Potential Electromagnetic Compatibility Problems in New Equipment and Existing Systems: The Hummer Test." *J. Audio Eng. Soc. (Engineering Reports).* 43: 484—487 (1995 June).

11

REMOTE CONTROL

SYSTEMS

by **L. WILLIAM NATTRESS III**

L. William Nattress III is a
Senior Associate with
Shen Milsom and
Wilke, Inc., Chicago.
He can be reached at
bnattress@chi.smwinc.com.

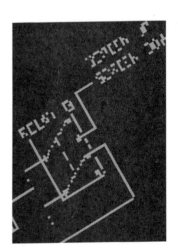

Integration is the practice of bringing together multiple products or devices into a unified system that operates as one. This is the primary task involved in the installation of audio-visual systems. Whether there are three devices or a hundred, the final product is integrated to allow an individual to communicate information to many people in the most effective manner. As technology advances there is a pervasive need to provide easy ways for non-technical operators to operate the components, whether one or many. This is made possible by the remote control system. This section will define the basic elements of remote control system design and the information required appropriately to integrate control components into an integrated system.

What is a remote control system?

Remote control systems actually are defined by the many tasks they perform, depending on the needs of the system. Their functional intent covers a broad scope of possibilities but can be broken down into five basic categories: device operation at a distance; device operation from multiple locations; multiple device integration; device automation; and simplicity of operation.

Device operation at a distance: When electric lights were first introduced it would have been impractical, and dangerous, to expect users to screw in a light bulb whenever they needed it illuminated. By placing a switch by the entry door to a room, a rudimentary control system was achieved, enabling users to turn on a light bulb conveniently as they enter the room.

Device operation from multiple locations: Continuing our example of the electric light, when rooms have more than one entry point the complexity of the system increases to allow users to turn the light on or off from each entry. In electrical terminology this is defined as a three-way switch for two control locations and a four-way switch when there are three points.

Multiple device integration: Within a home entertainment system many components are brought together. This is an excellent example to which many can relate because we are accustomed to having to deal with a handheld, infrared, remote control for each device in the system. This clutter of remotes can be addressed by the use of an all-in-one control that is programmed to operate all devices within the system, providing a single point for operators to use when they wish to interact with the system.

Device automation: As systems become more extensive, a remote control system can be employed to manage multiple tasks with a single button press. To watch the Sunday evening news, an operator must 1) turn on the television, 2) turn on the cable TV tuner and 3) switch the television to the cable TV input. Macros are created to allow a multiple item script to occur, enabling the operator to accomplish all three steps by pressing just one button. In the case of a presentation facility, multiple item scripts allow presenters to think about their presentations without having to worry about all of the steps required to present them.

Simplicity of operation: Not everyone is technically adept, nor has every individual using a system been trained in its operation. A remote control system can simplify all of the complex functions and steps needed to complete a specific task. When all aspects of a system have been designed correctly, the operation becomes seamless for anyone to use.

The first step in designing a remote control system

Control system design should begin at the same time that any integrated system is designed. The needs of the operator will define the technologies necessary to achieve the operator's goal. As display and source devices are selected, their control requirements and operational characteristics must be considered to provide the operator with the necessary application solutions. In some instances the application will require a specific control scenario that will need very specific components not typically utilized.

For a control system to operate, the device must allow itself to be controlled. This connection is called the control point. A port on the remote control system is connected to the device's control point via a link that is dependent on the type of control solution the device employs. Each type of control point has specific parameters and limitations that must be observed during the selection of components. From the remote control system port a physical connection is made to the control point of the device. This connection, referred to as the interface, may be physical or wireless, depending upon the technology employed.

In the simplest forms of control, such as the light switch example noted earlier, a message is sent from the control port through the interface to the controlled device. In more complex devices the interface allows bi-directional communication between the devices.

Types of control points: At this point in the evolution of technology, there are no standard or fixed classes of control points. Every remote control system manufacturer utilizes countless resources in keeping current with all manufacturers' control point types, required interfaces and necessary language protocols. The most common control points are identified here.

Control Point Type I—Contact Closure. The contact closure is the simplest form of remote control communication. This type of control point provides device operation by closing an electrical current or voltage loop and has the most basic protocol language of On (closed circuit) and Off (open circuit). Such protocol language is the basis of binary logic systems represented by 0's and 1's, off and on respectively.

Typically mechanical devices, such as motors, are what contact closures control. Projection screens, drapes and shades require a low voltage interface to allow the low voltage of the contact closure to operate the high or line voltage of the motor.

Use of a contact closure is not limited to the control of a device; it also can provide input to the control system. In the earlier example, a single switch can be used to turn on a light within the room. In more advanced systems, the contact closure can provide the status of a room dividing panel or be installed within a door jamb to turn on the light when the door is opened.

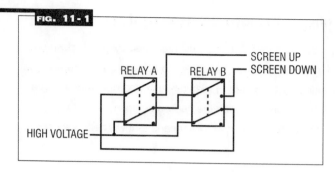

FIG. 11-1

- The interlock—Contact closure control requires a single contact for each function to be controlled. In the case of a projection screen or shade system, one contact is needed for the up function and another for down. An interlock is a protection feature which ensures that the up and down functions are not applied simultaneously. Typically the low voltage interface provides the electrical circuit protection, but good system design and programming practices also will provide this protection. In the example circuit shown in Figure 11-1, Relay B will not have any voltage when Relay A is turned on and vice versa. The two relays are interlocked.

- Binary Coded Decimal (BCD)— As indicated above, the contact closure is the basis of binary logic systems. By bringing together multiple closures, values can be calculated using binary math. Each switch represents a binary value: 1, 2, 4, 8, 16, 32, 64, 128. In the example in Figure 11-2, the closed switches represent the value of 42 since switches 2, 4, and 6 are closed. With eight switches the BCD system can count from 0 to 255.

A Binary Coded Decimal
(BCD) circuit

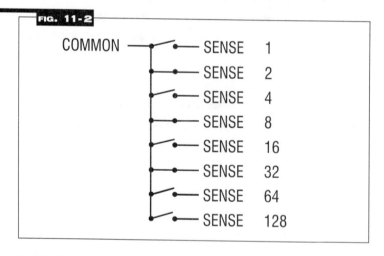

FIG. 11-2

Control Point Type II—Variable Voltage Control. The variable voltage control, also referred to as a voltage ramp generator, is an analog form of data control. A voltage of specific parameters is applied to the control point of the device to adjust a level by a specific ratio of voltage value to device level.

Early versions of light dimming system technology used this form of control to dim the lighting. A 0 to 24 VDC signal was applied to the dimming system zone or light circuit and the lighting was illuminated at the same percentage. If a 12 VDC signal was applied, for example, the lights were illuminated at 50 percent.

Other types of devices that control via a variable voltage signal are pan/tilt heads and servo motor controls. Typically these devices work in the same fashion as the dimming systems but also can operate in a reference voltage condition. When 0 volts are applied to the unit it is at rest; if a negative voltage is applied it will move in one direction, while a positive voltage will cause it to move in the other.

An important design criterion for any variable voltage control device is voltage drop. Wire length and gauge will affect the output voltage at the end of the line and thus affect the operation of the device. The equation in Figure 11-3 provides the values needed for input voltage once the cable type and length are known. Cable loss can create a situation that requires the control port to be located in very close proximity to the device being controlled.

FIG. 11-3

$$\frac{\text{Input}}{\text{voltage}} = \frac{\text{Output}}{\text{voltage}} - \left(\underset{\text{(amps)}}{I} \times \underset{\text{(feet)}}{\text{Wire length}} \times 2 \times \underset{\text{(ohms / foot)}}{R} \right)$$

Cable voltage loss equation

Control Point Type III—Infrared. Infrared control comes in two formats: optical and wired. The optical format is what is used by the typical handheld remote found in most homes to control the television set. The wired format generally is referred to as serial communication, along with many other names created by individual manufacturers. The serial communication format sends the same information pulses that would be sent if it were an infrared control, but bypasses the optical circuitry.

The communication parameters of each remote control are captured and learned by the control ports or special devices that save a file for insertion into the remote control system program. These files are available from the control system manufacturers and provide a detailed list of the functions that can be controlled on a device.

■ Infrared Control—A pattern of light pulses is emitted from a light emitting diode (LED) in the light spectrum that is just beyond the view of the human eye. These light pulses form patterns that are recognized by the control point on the device. If the light patterns do not match the specific functions programmed into the controlled device the function is ignored.

The advantages of infrared control are that it is very inexpensive to manufacture and simple to integrate into many control technologies, from the all-in-one type hand-held controls up to the most complex control system mainframe devices.

Optical infrared solutions do have disadvantages however. This control type requires direct line of sight to the device's control point and is limited to a 30-40-foot range. Optical repeaters and infrared blasters can be employed to overcome these limitations. Additionally most integrated remote control systems infrared ports employ IR LEDs that are installed directly over the controlled device's IR receiver or control point. This allows control of the device while it is installed within a cabinet or equipment rack.

Another disadvantage of optical infrared is that the signal is susceptible to interference from sunlight or fluorescent lighting. In environments where this cannot be controlled, the wired serial format provides remote control of the device. It also provides a cleaner installation, as there are no devices attached onto the front panel of the component. The wired solution provides the ability to be wired up to 250 feet from the control system.

Either control link also is limited to a one-way communication path. This means that the infrared controlled device has no way to provide feedback on its status or confirmation that it has received a command from the control system.

■ Discrete Codes—The infrared control protocols come in three varieties; toggle functions, stacked functions and discrete functions. Using the common television set as an example we can illustrate these three protocol types.

The handheld remote control with a television usually has a single button for power. Press the button and the TV turns on; press it again and the TV turns off. This is a toggling function. It requires additional control components to sense that the power is actually on. Different sensing devices are available from every remote control system manufacturer and should be selected based on the specific device being controlled, and its manufacturer.

Stacked functions are features that roll from one to the next through an available list, and start over again from the beginning of the list when the end is reached. The television remote will have a button labeled "Input," and pressing that button will switch the TV from the available inputs in a specific order—Input 1, Input 2, Input 3 (front panel), Tuner and then back to Input 1. Since the infrared control solution has only one-way communication, there is no way to verify what the present setting within the stacked function is. Attempting to automate a stacked function control typically is not advised as the possibility of getting the control system and the controlled device out of sync is quite high.

Discrete codes solve the difficulties of both toggled and stacked functions because a separate control pattern is available for each function. Power on and power off are separate buttons, as are each of the input selections. Discrete codes provide a greater control capability on the device, allowing a higher level of automation, although there still is no return path to the control system to verify that the specific code was received. In mission critical environments, best industry practices avoid the use of infrared control links due to this inability to receive device feedback.

Control Point Type IV—Radio Frequency. Radio frequency (RF) control generally is employed as a user interface to the control system. Some manufacturer's devices provide control links into their components using RF transmission, as this affords the ability to control devices when line of site is not possible. Third-party remote control system manufacturers do not easily emulate this type of control link, as it requires specific frequencies of communication along with the protocol with which to communicate.

An important design element when using RF control scenarios is verification of the frequencies already in use or that are noisy within the environment to be controlled. The radio frequency spectrum is quite busy, and many electronic components release stray RF into the environment that can interfere with the desired communication packets. By testing the spaces to be controlled, appropriate frequencies can be implemented that will function properly.

Control Point Type V—Digital Data. Digital data control points represent the most diverse and prolific communications format available for controlling higher level functions of system components. Packets of digital information, or the devices protocol, are best described as commuting traffic on a highway. Individuals drive different types of vehicle onto different expressways or roads to get to their final destination. In data communications, the protocol sent and received is the cars, and their specific information is the color, number of doors and number of passengers they may contain. When a vehicle reaches its destination, the controlled device receives the specific information and responds by sending another car down the highway with new data, or simply an acknowledgement that the data were processed.

The roads and highways that data travel face the same challenges that exist in real world transportation. Rules are created allowing the traffic to flow more easily, as well as definitions of how the data "cars" will travel and on what types of roads. These defined traffic routes are synonymous with the types of digital communication formats available for control and the wiring schemes that they employ—single-ended, broadcast and multi-drop.

■ Single-ended digital data control—Single-ended digital control is a bi-directional communications path between two devices. A device transmits a packet of information to another that is the receiver. If the control configuration only requires transmission from one to reception of the other, then only two wire conductors are required—data signal and ground. This scenario is similar to infrared control in that there is no feedback provided from the control component. To achieve this feedback, a two-lane highway is necessary requiring three wire conductors—a data send, receive and ground. More sophisticated single-ended control devices require more conductors, depending on the type of data configuration and how the device handles the flow of data, whether with hardware or software.

■ Broadcast digital data control—Devices that utilize the broadcast topology of control are characterized by a single transmitting device with multiple receivers on the same wire bus. This communications structure typically is used only between devices of the same manufacturer. Each receiving device has a distinct address defined by software, hard switches or wiring order. The device listens to all information transmitted onto the bus and acts only upon information that begins with its specific address, ignoring all other data traveling on the line.

■ Multi-drop digital data control—Both broadcast and single-ended control solutions have inherent limitations that the multi-drop configuration resolves. Multi-drop allows multiple transmitters and receivers to share the same wire conductors, and the communications between the devices occurs simultaneously. Individual components can send and receive data like the bi-directional single-ended systems, but each is addressed separately as in the broadcast configuration. This scenario allows very complex networks of control information to be created.

Every type of digital data control fits into one of these three control scenarios. Knowing what type of scenario the devices utilize helps to define the architecture of the wiring design. The final piece of information required in creating the digital data control highway is what formats of digital data need to be addressed.

■ RS-232C—The most common form of digital data control is the EIA standard RS-232C. This single-ended topology standard defines only the electrical characteristics required for the communication, not the actual software protocol to be utilized. The protocol employed, as with all digital data communications, is defined by each manufacturer and changes from device to device.

The RS-232C standard is an unbalanced circuit and thus is susceptible to noise causing lost packets of information. This noise issue limits the control line to about 50'. Line filtering and cable type can extend this distance, but these solutions can require slower transmission speeds, less than 9,600 baud in many instances.

RS-232C communication most often is connected using the DB9 or DB25 connector types, and the pin-out of these connectors follows two types of configuration, Data Communications Equipment (DCE) and Data Terminal Equipment (DTE). The output of a DTE device is designed to go to the input of a DCE port. When connecting a DTE device to a DCE device a straight- through cable pin-out is utilized. Some control configurations require the interconnection of two DCE devices. A crossing of the transmit and receive lines is required in this circumstance; this is sometimes called a null modem configuration, this also will change the gender of the connectors.

The DTE to DCE wiring scheme

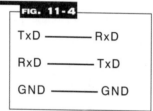

The DCE to DCE wiring scheme

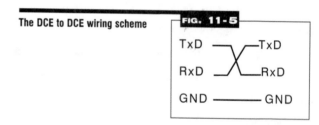

■ RS-422—The EIA standards recognize that the unbalanced characteristics of the RS-232C format do not allow for longer distance cable runs. Out of this realization the RS-422 standard was developed, providing a balanced, four-wire solution allowing cable runs of 2,000' to 6,000'. The length is dependent upon data speed and cable quality. RS-422 also expands on the RS-232C standard in that it can broadcast to as many as 10 devices.

■ RS-485—This standard is the multi-drop version of the EIA standards supporting a maximum of 256 transmitting and receiving devices. The multi-drop design allows cable distances up to 4,000' on unshielded twisted pair cable, and can be accomplished on only two wires due to its ability to utilize half-duplex communication protocols.

■ Other forms of digital data control—The three previously listed communication links are the most common utilized for control, but hundreds of other forms exist. The USITT DMX512 standard is used for lighting and show control systems, enabling 512 separate devices to be controlled on a single bus. Since lighting control requires high voltage dimming, the standard was developed to be immune to EMF interference.

X10 control, also known as power line carrier (PLC) control, broadcasts control sequences via a modulated signal on standard 120 VAC power circuits. This control solution is very popular within the home automation markets but can be challenging to implement, as it is susceptible to EMI/RFI problems. Another popular communications link within the automated home is the Dual Tone Multiplexed Frequency (DTMF) protocol. This signaling solution was developed by the telecommunications industry and is what is used to dial a telephone. The protocol allows control access via a standard telephone handset and is used to control custom programmed devices within the home as well as PBX and voice mail functions in corporate markets.

SMPTE time code is an analog 2,400Hz square wave signal utilized to maintain audio synchronization with film and video. This control protocol gets its name from the organization that developed it, the Society of Motion Picture and Television Engineers. Control scenarios utilizing SMPTE time code typically involve the access of specific locations within video content, making a very popular control solution for museum and pre-staged presentation environments.

Control Point Type VI—Ethernet. The most recent innovation in the control system arsenal is the use of standard Ethernet network topologies. This connection type could easily be defined as a digital data link, but the ramifications of its use are so extensive that it resides in a control point classification of its own. This is because digital data communication is designed to communicate between devices, while the Ethernet solution allows communication among control components, applications, data and the Internet.

Ethernet topologies are utilized mostly to extend the control environment at distances previously unimagined. Within a single building the local area network (LAN) can be employed to allow a central control room to communicate with each presentation room. LANs are connected together between buildings within a corporate campus to create a metropolitan area network (MAN). The LANs and MANs of individual organizations located within multiple cities are connected together, creating a wide area network (WAN). From these IT- based topologies control solutions can be created that allow effective real time room support, loss prevention, facility usage and scheduling, and web centric presentation environments, to name only a few possibilities. Within this environment, the control scenario shifts from the needs of the facility to enterprise- wide application specifics.

The second step in remote control system design

At this point the needs or application requirements of an integrated environment have been defined, allowing the designer to select the devices and their appropriate control port components. The layout process begins when the control system to device as well as the control system-to-system connections are identified. Three categories of control system topologies exist, each providing greater levels of sophistication as needed by the final integrated environment.

The centralized processing solution: The simplest and most common form of remote control system connects all of the components within a room or suite of rooms to a single master control processor. All these control ports are negotiated by the integrated processor's proprietary network solution, and most often are based on an RS-485 multi-drop digital data link. The single CPU runs a custom program to accept the input or control requests from the operator, and then controls the individual devices as required by that program.

The centralized processing topology

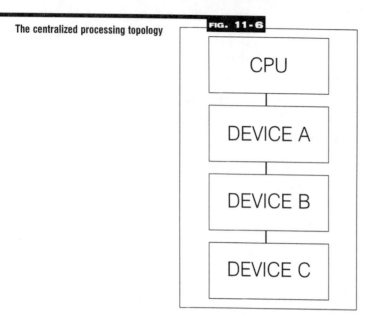

FIG. 11-6

The Client/Server solution: The client/server topology, also referred to as the master/slave configuration, provides a system configuration that utilizes multiple CPU frames, although only one CPU contains the custom program. This CPU acts as the master or server to all other CPUs, or clients, on the system. These client devices receive their instructions from the server and do not process any information. The drawback to this system configuration is that if the link between the client and server devices is broken, the client does not have the capability to continue functioning.

The client/server topology

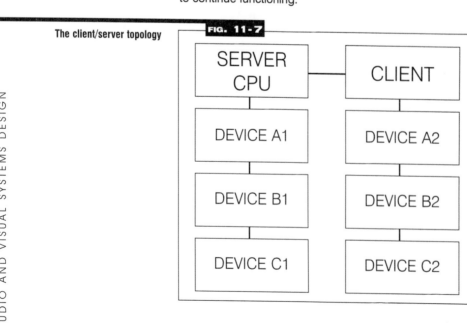

FIG. 11-7

The distributed processing solution:

Distributed processing of control system integration takes many central processing solutions and ties them all together utilizing an Ethernet-based link. The solution allows each integrated system to act autonomously while also providing interaction between systems. Since each processor has its own program and operational capabilities, it will continue

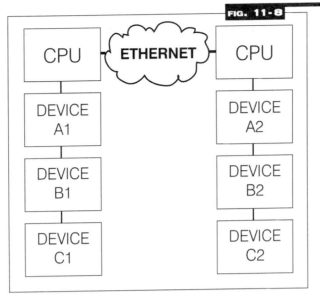

FIG. 11-8

The distributed processing topology

to operate even when the link between processors is broken.

Once the overall integrated system design has been identified, each component within the system is placed onto the flow diagram and connected to the nearest CPU or client control frame. The connections are made to the appropriate port type, based upon the individual components control port type as identified above.

The third step in remote control system design

Each device within the system has a specific set of functions. These functions can be as simple as the up, down and stop of a projection screen or as complex as the features of a tape transport—play, stop, pause, fast forward, rewind and record. Not every solution will require the use of every available device function. The needs and purpose of integrating the system will dictate what functions must be controlled within the environment.

An important step in the design process is to list each function necessary to operating the individual components. This step ensures that all of the operational parameters are met within the integrated environment. The functionality list aids the designer in providing information to the system engineer and control system programmers, so that the design intent of the systems is achieved.

The fourth step in remote control system design

Any and all remote control systems require some form of user interface. These devices come in many forms, based upon their intended function. The simplest form could be a button panel installed at the entry door of a presentation room allowing an operator to select a lighting level for the room. Advanced user interfaces involve graphically driven touch-sensitive screens or web-based control panels. The needs of the integrated solution will dictate the appropriate user interface device. What is most important to remember is that an inappropriately designed user interface will cause every integrated system to fail because the remote control system will not afford the operator the ability to control the environment as planned, designed or dictated by the needs of the solution.

In his book *The Design of Everyday Things*, Dr. Donald Norman identified the seven design goals of every user interface. These design goals provide questions that designers need to ask as they develop the user interface. The goals can be paraphrased as follows:

How easily can the user—
1. Determine the function of the system?
2. Tell what actions are possible?
3. Tell if the system is in the desired state?
4. Determine mapping from intention to physical movement?
5. Perform the action?
6. Determine mapping from system state to interpretation?
7. Tell what state the system is in?

Each of the aforementioned questions speaks to individual components of the user interface design. How easily can one identify how to turn on the system or play a videotape? Does this transport allow for recording, or is it intended only for playback? Does the system require navigating multiple menu pages, or can the operator switch from device to device without moving back up a menu tree?

General rules for user interface design: Nothing is cast in stone when it comes to designing user interfaces, as each system has a custom purpose. A few simple rules can be followed to allow any novice to control the functions of the integrated environment.

The first rule is to allow the operator to complete any function with only two button presses. Remember the purposes of remote control systems: distance, multi-point, multi-device, automation and simplification. To display a document camera, the operator needs to turn on the display device, lower the projection screen, select the appropriate input on the display device, route the document camera to that input and dim the lights to an appropriate setting. This entire chain of events can be achieved by pushing one button labeled Document Camera. The second button could select the location to which the document camera is connected. Systems could even be integrated to the point of sensing what input the document camera is connected to and automatically routing the signal.

Rule two is that the more important functions of any device should be more prominent on the interface. When designing presentation devices using transports, the Play and Stop functions are the most critical to the operator. These two functions should be made more prominent in the design, either by being placed first in order, or by being larger in size.

The third rule is that like functions should always appear in the same location on every page so that the operator does not need to hunt them down. If the Play function exists on the upper left of the VCR page, it should appear in the same location on every other page requiring transport functions.

Prior to the development of graphical user interfaces, hard button panels were employed to operate the system. These panels help in defining the fourth rule and achieving the seventh design goal. When controlling the power of a device, typically two buttons are employed, On and Off. With a hard button panel, each button has an LED associated with it. An operator can easily tell if the device is on by seeing the LED illuminated by the On button. Graphical user interfaces, whether monochrome or color, must use different ways to identify the state of a component. In our example, the device is presently on and the On button is colored red while the Off button is green. Does this truly tell the operator the actual state of the device? The fourth rule, then, is to maintain the same color or button fill throughout the interface design to indicate a feature is active.

The last rule in this short list is to avoid nesting menus. Navigation between system components should be accomplished by menu buttons on the user interface. Requiring an operator to select a menu item, then scroll through two pages to get to the desired function causes the operator momentarily to think about the presentation system and not the presentation. A standard device feature should always be available immediately, while advanced functions can be hidden to avoid very complex or busy pages.

System functional description: The functional description of a system is a document that defines the operation of the control system environment. This description is sometimes referred to as the Button-By-Button description or program flow diagram. When properly assembled, the descriptive document provides a means to identify the system to the end user prior to any programming and, once approved, provides the information needed by the programmer to code the system. Lastly, this document can be incorporated into the operations manual provided to the customer for future reference and training on the system.

An appropriate functional description of a system defines the automated tasks built into each button press, the conditional data or actions that the system may need to consider prior to performing an action, and the feedback parameters required to allow the operator easily to ascertain the state of the system. The description to control a particular device within an integrated environment typically will be the same from room to room and project to project. Most successful programmers and integrators create a library of programming solutions that contains the custom code, description and design criteria for each device type. This library allows integration by very efficient means and provides standardization that aids in supporting the system long after it is installed.

12

VIDEOCONFERENCING

by SCOTT SHARER, CTS, AND JIM SMITH, CVE

Scott Sharer, CTS, founder of Communication Design Group and Logical Transitions, is widely recognized for his design and engineering work on sophisticated communication systems and new product designs, and for his own innovative and effective use of the technology of videoconference .

Jim Smith, CVE, is an engineering consultant in the field of audio-video communications and currently is working with one of the largest videoconferencing manufacturers, training integrators in the use of this technology. He can be reached at smithj@barkharbor.com.

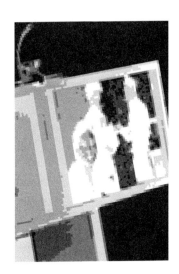

In many ways the application of conference technology to traditional presentation and meeting spaces seems like a natural extension of both the use of the spaces and the technology that has been integrated within them. (For the purpose of this discussion, we will consider the term *conferencing* to mean the more traditional concept of teleconferencing—implying an audio conference application—and videoconferencing, since this includes both audio and video, and the rules and "best practices" for deployment apply equally to both.)

While many readers might expect this to be a section on encoding AV and the modern forms and protocols of digital networks, it is not. The most concise discussion of network topics appears in the *Voice and Data Communications Handbook*, published by McGraw-Hill, a book of more than 750 pages! Aside from the impossibility of tackling such a topic in only a few pages, experience has demonstrated time and again that the encoding and transport of signals across the network actually is quite simple. That's right—it is simple, despite the fact that the forms and methods change every day as the global telephone network adapts, grows, migrates, morphs and weaves through our personal and business culture. The really tough part of successful conference deployment is found, instead, in the traditional elements of audio, video and room layout—all of the areas that we might have assumed are "no-brainers" for experienced AV and presentation professionals of today. Far from being "no-brainers," space planning and AV technology deployment are the great stumbling blocks of conferencing. Incomplete or incorrect planning and deployment on the room side of the conference equation lead to 99 percent of all failures to deliver on expectations in this most powerful of communications. Why that is and how to avoid this pitfall is the subject of this discussion.

For many people, the idea of a presentation space acting as a real-time videoconference presentation space appears to be a simple step in the general application of technical elements. If the space in question has been developed for live local presentation, with the now typical elements of large screen projection of video and computer sources; live interaction and drawing via a whiteboard or flip chart; and the ability to display the audio portion of any video element, along with, perhaps, voice reinforcement of the local presenter, then it is easy to assume that all we need to add is a camera to show the live image of the presenter, and some sort of A-D digitizer (codec or COder-DECoder) attached to a network, to transport the information to another location. With those additions, the assumption is that we are ready to conference. That assumption is the result of traditional audiovisual thinking, which pigeonholes conferencing into a narrow subset of presentation. Anyone who has encountered this approach knows, however, how deficient the end-result will be when judged in the context of the ability of an end-user to achieve live two-way communication between two or more geographically dispersed groups.

For both those who implement and those who use the systems, videoconferencing (VC) is a far less forgiving medium than one intended for in-person meeting and presentation. Small oversights in planning videoconferencing systems can result in devastating consequences.

We also find that the elements that have the greatest influence on the success for the end-user of a videoconference system are determined at the outset by the space planner and AV systems provider.

It is very useful to consider the proper planning and deployment of videoconferencing within the context of the separate elements of room or space plan, and AV elements.

VC room or space planning

For clarity of discussion, we have divided this section into the following sub-sections:

- Room construction, including wall construction, windows and window treatments, ceilings and HVAC;
- Interior design and finishes;
- Furniture design, including placement and layout;
- Room acoustics and acoustic treatment; and
- Room lighting.

The initial layout and construction of the space affects all the elements that are discussed in other sections of this book, including acoustic characteristics and performance, general and ambient light control, and overall comfort.

Room requirements

We begin with general room requirements. The total floor space required for VC is much greater than we have become used to for general local presentation and meeting. In architectural terms it is not uncommon to find a rule-of-thumb applied that allows for up to 15 square feet of floor space per participant in a traditional presentation or meeting room. If there is a front-of-room presenter position at a podium, and if there is some use of in-room technology (projection devices, whiteboards, etc.), then this figure may increase to as much as 20 square feet of floor space per participant, but rarely any more than that.

It is here that we have our first conflict. In videoconferencing we have to consider not only the issues related to local viewing and hearing but also the issues of being seen and heard by people at the far-end of the connection. This means that we must consider sight lines and angles of participant interaction that go beyond traditional presentation environments. As a rule we should allow not less than 30 square feet and generally not more than 45 square feet of floor space per participant in a videoconference space. Though two to three times what we are used to allowing, this amount ensures that local participants will see one another and the display of local and remote electronic images. It also ensures that participants at the far-end will see and hear everyone arriving at their location via the connection, and that all will see and hear at a level of quality that does not detract and, in the best deployment, even enhances the communications.

Having determined the required size of the space, we can move on to the actual renovation or construction of the space itself. Again the requirements here are generally less forgiving than those applied in local-only meeting spaces. In the most basic sense this is because, by sheer definition, at least some of the participants in a conference-based meeting are not actually in the room. As such, we cannot count on the typical human mechanisms (the human ears and brain and our ability to locate sound in three-dimensional space) to manage any acoustic anomalies.

If we are, for example, in a room that is adjacent to a double-door entry to the building, then knowing this we can take the inevitable doorway noise into account as we filter the sounds we hear both inside the meeting room and coming from that adjacent entryway. Within our own physical and local environment we have the ability to isolate local unwanted noise from local "sound of interest" (voices of other people, etc.), and place the unwanted noise in an inferior position in our conscious thought pattern. We are able to do this because we know where the noise is coming from and (usually) what is causing it. We may be annoyed by the noise, but we generally are able to ignore it. As soon as we add conferencing to the meeting equation, however, we add the element of electronic pickup and reproduction of all sounds. For the people at the far-end, the unwanted noise is much more difficult (if not impossible) to ignore. They do not have the ability to isolate it in three-dimensional space (the microphones eliminate the spatial reference) and they often do not know what is making the noise. The brain of the far-end participant will devote more and more conscious observation and thought energy to trying to work out these elements, in an attempt to isolate and finally "ignore" the unwanted sound. We have already stated that they cannot do this, however, due to the electronic separation between the locations. Thus they are left with an impossible task that takes up more and more thought energy, eroding the perceived quality of the spoken communication over time. Frustration and exasperation quickly set in, and the communication flow quickly falls apart.

This, then, is one reason we must pay even greater attention to the acoustic and visual issues for any presentation space that will be connected via conference to another. Minor, seemingly insignificant anomalies we often ignore in the local environment become significant impediments to smooth communication with people at the far-end of any connection. In short, we must always ask ourselves, "What does this look like and sound like to the people at the far-end?"

In order to guarantee that the final conference environment will have a solid foundation, we begin with the construction of the walls, floors and ceilings for videoconference spaces.

Walls: Conference room walls should be built from slab to slab. That is, there should be no gaps from the concrete of one floor to the concrete of the next floor. Resilient, gypsum board mountings should be used to close any gaps. The thickness of the gypsum board should be $5/8$" or more (one layer of $5/8$" and one layer of $1/2$" bonded together would be ideal) on the inside of the room, with $1/2$" thick (or as required by local building codes) appropriate for the outside of the walls. There should always be a difference in thickness between the materials used on the inner versus the outer walls. That difference in thickness subdues mechanical coupling (vibration) between the two layers. A good overall wall thickness is 6". It is recommended that "offset stud" construction be used, typically a 6" header and footer with 3.5" verticals attached in an alternating pattern one toward the outside of the footer, the next toward the inside and so on.

Fiberglass dense batting or mineral rock wool, 4" to 6" thick (the equivalent of R-11 to R-13) should be placed in the wall space. The thickness of the batting is not critical. The critical aspect is that it must be loosely placed in the wall space, not compacted to fit. The resultant wall will have excellent acoustic isolation from the outside world. More significant acoustic isolation can be achieved by placing an additional barrier layer within the wall space. Typically this barrier will be made of a dense polymer material, about $1/8$" thick, and the improvement regarding loss of sound transmitted through the wall will be roughly a factor of 10. These materials are available from a variety of manufacturers.

Windows: Windows usually present the equivalent of an acoustic nightmare (as well as altering the way a camera renders colors and brightness). They not only transmit room sound, but also allow unwanted outside noise to intrude on the conference space. In the event that windows cannot be avoided, it becomes essential that window treatment of some sort be used. This treatment should match the interior look and feel of the space, while providing a high level of sound and light block. Typically a heavyweight drape (24 ounces or more) of heavy fullness (not less than 6" fullness on not less than 8" centers per fold) is preferred. In all cases, the use of sheer draperies or standard vertical or horizontal blinds should be avoided, due to their inherent inefficiency in blocking sound and light, and the fine lines they create within the camera field of view.

Ceiling tiles: These should be high-quality acoustic tiles, ideally 1"- thick compressed dense-core fiberglass. An added benefit of this kind of ceiling tile is that it works well with the indirect lighting as specified elsewhere in this section. To reduce any extraneous noise from leaving or entering the room via the ceiling space, the ceiling tiles can be blanketed completely from the plenum side, with a minimum of 6"- thick unfaced dense fiberglass batting or mineral rock wool, (the equivalent of R-15 to R-19). Here again, a barrier layer will improve the performance, but all local building codes must be followed for allowable materials in the various aspects of room acoustic modifications. To make entry and exit from the ceiling space easier, the blanket and barrier do not need to rest on the ceiling tiles, but may be suspended above it.

Air conditioning: It is critical that all air-handling equipment (blowers, heat exchangers, solenoid valves, etc.) be located outside the physical meeting room space. This will prevent the noise burden associated with such equipment from affecting the participants of any meetings held in the room. Location of air-handling equipment within the ceiling space of a conference room often renders that room unusable for video or audio-only conferencing.

The air vents should be of open construction to eliminate "wind noise" while the system is running. These vents normally are specified as "low-velocity" diffusers. The number of air vents within the room should be sufficient to maintain a consistent temperature throughout the space. All HVAC ducts and diffusers should be oversized for the general application in the space, with minimum 2' diameter insulated flexible ducts and matching 2' noise dampening diffusers generally best. All ducts should be installed with gradual bends and curves rather than rigid 90-degree corners. This will minimize "thunder" sounds as the initial air pushes through the ductwork and into the room.

There should be a thermostat to control this specific room system independently of the rest of the building, and that control should be located within the room.

Important: Allow an additional 5,000 BTU of cooling capacity for a standard "roll-about" single-monitor VC system with extended in-room peripherals (PC, document camera, scan converter, etc.) and a minimum of 10,000 BTU for a dual display multimedia presentation system with large screen displays. For the comfort of the participants, the room must accommodate these heat loads, plus the heat load of a room full of people, with minimal temperature rise.

Interior design and finishes

Wall colors within the field of view of the camera have a significant impact on the far-end perception of the room video quality. Certain colors are better suited to video rooms than others. The electronics and software of the videoconferencing system "builds" the images at the far-end from a gray/blue reference image. When there is a minimal difference between the room background and the reference image color, the codec has an easier time turning the image into numbers, with the result that the far-end will see a much higher quality video presentation. In general, light gray with just a touch of blue seems to work best. For rooms that have marginal lighting, slightly darker colors are quite useful.

In keeping with these color recommendations, the acoustic panels (discussed elsewhere in this section) should be ordered in light colors such as silver-gray, quartz or champagne for panels within the camera field of view. For aesthetics, however, panels may be alternated in color along the wall.

Furniture: As we have noted, VC rooms should be slightly on the large side for the typical number of attendees. The placement of furniture should present a natural rapport with the videoconference system, but shouldn't preclude the local interaction of conference participants. Doorways used for access to the space usually should be within the view of one of the camera presets to prevent the perception from the far-end that people could come into their meeting unseen. Doorways should not, however, be in constant, direct view of the camera system, as this may cause unwanted distractions and movement of people in the picture field.

Any tables within the conference environment should have a light top surface. Glossy tops should be avoided, as should strong colors or any bold wood grain. If glossy or saturated color surfaces are unavoidable, then proper lighting can help reduce (but not necessarily eliminate) their ill effects. The best table surface color is a flat satin finish, in neutral gray. In cases where the worst possible surfaces are present, the proper surface color effect can be achieved by using a table covering, put in place only when the room is being used for videoconferencing. This will, however, create problems related to the use of access ports in the tables or movement of end-user items across the surface.

Acoustics

Additional general elements related to the interior finish details for the space include acoustics. In terms of ambient noise level, the acoustic design goal for any conference- enabled room is at least NC-30 (NoiseCriteria-30). This level of specification dictates a very quiet space (somewhere around 40-dBCSPL ambient noise level). A room built to the description found elsewhere in this section will usually fall between NC-30 and NC-35. The actual NC value is not critical; what is important is that the room be built with the intent and care required to achieve the low noise rating. Typically in architectural design, a site evaluation and analysis are required to certify the noise performance of a given space. The quieter the room, the easier it is to hear others in the same room as well as be heard by others who are participating via conference connection to a far-end location (or locations).

Almost every conference room of medium to large size (larger than 12'x15') requires some level of acoustic treatment to provide good speech-rendering to other conference sites. The quality differences lie in the areas of intelligibility and consistency of loudness as presented to the far-end. While the people at the far-end may hear the sounds coming to them, it may be hard for them clearly to distinguish all of the vowels, consonants, inflections and nuances of actual human speech communication. (We all know that it is not simply what you say but how you say it—i.e., the inflections and intonations—that makes the difference in perceived meaning in human communications.)

Good audio practice dictates that the treated surfaces be composed of at least two nonparallel walls. And, as the VCS hardware is a potential source of distracting fan noises, the walls to be treated should include the wall immediately behind the VCS hardware, whenever this hardware is within the conference room proper. To help prevent meeting audio from leaking into adjoining hallways or offices, the walls along those areas also should be treated.

Approximately 50 percent of the wall area needs be covered with acoustic panels. The type recommended is 1" thick compressed, dense-core fiberglass, fabric-covered, or equivalent, with a SABIN (sound absorption index) value of 0.9 average. This specification is sometimes referred to as NRC (noise reduction coefficient). If reduction of sound passing through is required, then an additional barrier layer is laminated to the dense-core material, usually $3/8$" thick fiber compression board. The barrier layer is placed against the existing wall material, then the acoustic absorption panels are placed on the interior-room side of that. The barrier panels will have a SABIN of 0.9, but will have an additional specification of an STC (sound transmission coefficient) of 20. STC is a measure of the amount of reduction in loudness of sound passing through the material. Having an STC rating of 20 means there is a factor of 10 reduction in the amount of sound passing through that material. A high-quality conference room wall usually has an STC of 60 or more—that is, less than $1/1{,}000$ of the sound in the room leaks through the wall.

Room lighting

The brightness of the lighting in a videoconference room plays an important role in determining the far-end view of the meeting. When there are low to moderate amounts of light—20fc to 35fc (footcandles), typical office lighting—the distance range of "in focus" objects (depth-of-field) usually is only 2' or 3' from nearest in-focus to furthest in-focus. With bright light (70fc or more) the range of in-focus objects can more than double. Participants at the far-end will see more people in sharp focus, and the codec will have an easier time encoding the image.

Bright standard direct fluorescent lighting has the undesirable side effect of being harsh for the local participants. In addition, the direct down lighting casts significant "drop shadows." The result is undue stress among participants.

The best plan for videoconferencing is to use indirect lighting for 80 to 85 percent of the light, and evenly distributed direct lighting for the remaining 15 to 20 percent. The indirect light will help minimize shadows on the faces of the participants, and make the room more comfortable for viewing the far-end on the TV monitor. The direct light can be used to create backlight separation between foreground and background objects or surfaces.

There should be not less than 55fc and ideally as much as 75fc of light (770lux) on the faces of the participants in the facial field as viewed by the camera in the conference space. The light should be completely even across the field of measure or view, and of one consistent color temperature.

To best meet these requirements, indirect fluorescent lighting most often is recommended. This type of lighting works by using the upper walls and ceiling as diffuse reflectors for the light. The usual recommended color temperature for these is 3,000 to 3,800 degrees Kelvin. If there is a significant quantity of outdoor light entering the room, the lamps should be more than 5,500 degrees Kelvin.

Light fixtures: The light fixtures generally recommended for indirect lighting are available from a number of manufacturers. They typically are three-tube, 8" oval indirect up-lights, though they may take the form of chandelier-style pendant lights, wall sconces, cove lights or flush-mounted specialized troughs. Many manufacturers work closely with contractors and lighting designers to ensure that the correct light levels and shadow-free zones are designed into the room, especially when used for videoconferencing. Lamps for these fixtures are available in a variety of specified color temperatures from numerous manufacturers, including Sylvania, General Electric and Osram/Phillips. Indirect fixtures are available in a number of different designs or "looks," and can be purchased in configurations that will complement and not detract from the interior design of the space.

Lighting layout recommendations and determination of the number of fixtures needed are handled either by the architectural design firm or by submitting a complete floor plan, including reflected ceiling, walls and furniture placement, to fixture vendors. The vendors will analyze the plans and return a finished lighting layout to the customer, detailing the number of fixtures, placement and required wiring.

It is important to remember that the use of traditional meeting room downcans—even those that have color-corrected light sources—for any lighting in the field of view that may include human faces is to be avoided at all costs. These will result in extremely uneven fields of light, or pools, and heavy, unnatural shadows on the faces of the participants.

Room preparation conclusion: When we follow the above guidelines we dramatically improve the odds for success in the final deployment of live bi-directional conference-based human communications. An added benefit is that this approach dramatically enhances the effectiveness of the room as it operates for more traditional meetings and presentations. The environment is more comfortable and flexible, and less dependent on specialized electronics for "fixing" deficiencies in the environment.

Audio elements

Once the space is prepared, we can focus on integration of the various audiovisual tools within the environment: audio, video and control.

Audio input: The primary input device for the audio portion of any conference system is the microphone. Elsewhere in this book we have discussed how these devices operate within a given acoustic environment. We turn now to a short discussion of how these elements operate within a conference environment, where such factors as "three-to-one" rules and "critical distance" often are pushed to the limit or violated entirely.

When sound travels in a room, it follows "the inverse square law." This means that the sound level heard at a microphone drops by a factor of four every time the distance doubles. Another important consideration in room audio design is the concept of "critical distance," or the distance at which the loudness of the room background noise plus reverberation is less than one tenth of the loudness of voices getting to a particular microphone. (This definition is the result of research conducted by Don and Carolyn Davis. that is referenced in the chapter "Designing for Intelligibility" in the *Handbook for Sound Engineers.*[1])

As an example, we will work with a room having an ambient noise level of approximately 60dBA-SPL. A person speaking in a normal voice is 72dBA-SPL at about 2' distance. At 4' the loudness drops to approximately 66dBA-SPL. This already is farther than the critical distance criteria allow, given the ambient noise level. At 8' distance, a normal speaking voice is approximately 60dBA-SPL. Now the voice energy and the room background noise are about equal. For "send" audio systems in a room to work correctly, therefore, the room noise level would have to be below 40-45dBA-SPL at the microphones at all times. This gives us some measure by which we can begin to plan the microphone array within a space, including selection based on pickup pattern, sensitivity, noise rejection and signal-to-noise in relation to the ambient noise floor or level within the space. The good news is that a room designed and built as described in this section will provide an acoustic space where almost any properly configured and installed audio system can operate with very good results.

Perhaps the most difficult issue for any room designer or system planner is actual microphone placement within the space. Given the fact that many people view conference table space as sacred (to be used for papers, laptops, coffee cups and other end-user items), there often is a great deal of pressure to place the local microphones on the ceiling instead of on the table surface. But this approach must be taken with great caution. We have already seen the dramatic impact of changes in the distance between people (their mouths) and the microphone. Ceiling systems generally place microphones farther away from the participants' mouths, not closer; critical distance calculations may eliminate ceiling placement from consideration for this reason alone. In addition, the ceiling surface generally is one of the noisiest areas of the room. Proximity to HVAC ducts and vents, attachment of tiles and runners to building members that are prone to vibration and shaking, and proximity to noise from other spaces migrating through the plenum make this area one of the least desirable for placement of microphones. This doesn't, however, keep people from looking at this broad open surface as the best place for microphones, to "get them off the table."

If ceiling placement is chosen, the system planner must select the components with great care from a manufacturer that specializes in this type of audio voice reinforcement. The manufacturer must be skilled in live audio and capable of installing the components (that is, being both able and willing to locate microphones at precisely measured distances from speakers, and locating those speakers at precisely measured intervals from each other and from the walls) to extremely tight tolerances. The system provider must fully inform the end-users of the potential downside effects of this approach. In any event, simply mounting a standard tabletop microphone on the ceiling tiles or implementing this solution in an ambient noise environment of 45dBA-SPL or greater will all but guarantee costly failure. No amount of post-microphone processing will fix the problems.

Audio output: For conference communication we do not really care about producing the thundering roar of jet aircraft engines, or other sounds reproduced on TV or in the movies. We are interested in reproducing the human voice. The tone, intonation, pitch and level of people speaking from the far-end should sound as much as possible like the sound they would make if they were speaking in the room. Given what has been covered in other sections of this book, we will touch base here on a couple of simple, basic elements of the speaker technology we deploy in the conference room. These basics fall into three subcategories: direction, power and range/frequency response.

Direction: As human beings, we feel most comfortable when the voice we hear appears to come from the same direction as the image of the person speaking. This means that reliance on ceiling speakers alone is not an ideal practice when the system is used for videoconferencing. In many small and medium-sized systems, front-firing speakers alone can provide proper direction and adequate coverage. Larger rooms (greater than 12'x15') probably need both front-firing and side or top-fill speakers in order to maintain proper coverage at nominal power levels.

In planning systems for larger rooms, we need to take advantage of the HAAS effect. Basically stated, this is the human brain's interpretation of sound direction when the same sound arrives at the ear from two or more directions within a certain time period. We attribute the direction of the sound to the direction from which the sound is first perceived, even if it is mixed with that same sound arriving from a completely different direction, as long as the two (or more) instances of the sound are within about 30ms of one another. Since sound travels faster electronically than it travels through the open air we may need to add audio delay to the side firing or ceiling speaker arrays in order to keep the primary perceived point source as the front of room/front-firing speakers.

Power: Power is a function of loudspeaker efficiency and total available system power. Most speakers operate in a power range that is broader than the range in which they operate without distortion. For the purpose of conference communication, we are interested in sound that has little or no distortion. Sound that is reproduced accurately (with no distortion) will most accurately represent the voice of the people from the far-end (our primary goal). Accurate reproduction also will aid the echo-cancellation circuitry in the system, minimizing the amount of echo that the system sends back to the people at the far-end, and thereby increasing perceived ease of intelligibility and understanding. Remember that any distortions present in the playback audio system—whether harmonic, amplitude (gain compression) or temporal (time delays)—will be recognized by the echo canceller as "new audio information," and it will send those distortions to the far-end, perhaps wreaking havoc on the system audio quality. In short, speaker power should be matched to overall audio subsystem power. The speakers should provide adequate coverage and be able to present approximately 80 to 85dBA-SPL (continuous) at the local site with the system operating at nominal power utilization, and have a peak reserve of 15 to 20dB before distortion.

Range/ frequency response: The human ear is able to hear sounds in a very wide range of frequencies (as low as 70Hz and as high as 12,000Hz). The human voice is able to produce sounds in a narrower range (100Hz to 8,000Hz). Most spoken communication occurs, however, in a range that is only 150Hz to about 6,000Hz. This means that we need to select speakers that operate with ideal performance in a fairly narrow range for human voice (as opposed to speakers used for music, that may have ranges of 20Hz to 20,000Hz). We must also be alert to the crossover characteristics of the speakers we select. Many coaxial and paraxial speakers have their crossover within the middle audio frequencies, thereby inducing potential distortion within the spoken frequency range and creating anomalies within the system that hinder voice communication.

Video elements

As a general rule, any display used in a videoconferencing environment should be sized for the number of attendees, the physical distances involved and the type of material presented on-screen. The screen size should allow for clear and easy viewing at the various distances experienced within the room. A measure of required screen size that often is applied to projection technology is: no closer than 1.5 times the diagonal measure and no farther than 7 times that measure. Nobody should have to sit closer than 2 times the screen diagonal measure, nor farther than 8 times that measure.

Direct viewed tube-type displays (monitors) almost always are sharpest and brightest in a videoconferencing environment. "Retro-projector cabinet" displays (which look like large-screen TVs) are next in sharpness and brightness, and "front-screen" projectors come in last. Glare and uncontrolled ambient room lighting adversely affect the quality of the image most with front-screen projectors and least with direct view tubes. A very limited number of front-screen projection systems have sufficient brightness and contrast to be useful in a properly lit videoconference room.

Video projection for use in videoconference: Many installations make use of video projection devices. The most important thing to remember in the planning of video projection for a video-conference space is that front projection is vastly inferior to rear projection. Front projection systems are less expensive and easier to implement, but the conflicting interest between the camera and the projection display makes this form of display a very poor choice. Front projection setups operate best when the lighting in the room is dimmed or doused. When this is done, the videoconference cameras can no longer operate, since they require even, bright, color-corrected light. A direct conflict between these two technologies is clear. In the event that a rear projection room cannot be set aside, retro-projection units can be purchased from a number of manufacturers. These units normally are available in sizes ranging from 40" to 72" diagonal measure. To display high-quality video while maintaining optimum lighting for interactive video meetings will require a projector of the "light-valve" or DLP™ class.

Regardless of the exact type of projector selected and the exact nature of "front versus rear," there are certain essential rules for projector placement. The goal in projection is to get the image beam to aim directly into the audience's eyes. In Western cultures the average distance from the floor to a seated person's eye is 4'. That distance becomes the target for the direct beam of the projector. Again keep in mind that front projection should be avoided except in the most extreme cases. If it is employed at all it must be used with an extremely bright projector (2,500 lumens or greater for any space smaller than 25'x40').

Cameras: There usually is a "main" or "local people" camera positioned on top center of the display, so that it can "see" the participants and anything necessary at the sides of the room, using pan and tilt features. If individual presentations may be made from the side or "front of audience" area of the room, an additional camera should be located at the back of the room, also mounted to allow a view of the presenters when necessary. Some cameras contain an active camera pointing system that also can be used effectively, given proper care in the mounting of the camera assembly. The area immediately surrounding the camera assembly needs to be acoustically "dead" to ensure that the voice tracking and pointing algorithms work correctly. This is another reason to pay close attention to the acoustic environment and acoustic treatment of any space intended for use with this type of camera system.

If local presentation is blended with VC for any events, we must consider the needs of the presenter who will not be "facing" the local image or inbound image displays used by the main body of the local audience. One or two monitors (and a camera) should be mounted at the back of the "audience-end" of the room, with the horizontal centerline at approximately 5' from the floor for ease of presentation interaction between the presenter and the group(s) at the far-end(s). Remember that, with the exception of PC-based information that is not in a standard composite narrowband video format, any information we wish to "show" or "view" must be translated to video, most often with some sort of camera mechanism. Document cameras, 35mm slide-to-video units, video scanners and scan conversion devices all are designed to take one format of source material and convert it to a standard video signal that can be digitized, shipped to the far-end(s), and converted back to composite video for display. Which devices are selected and how they are used depends entirely on the needs and goals of the end-users of the system(s) and the format of their source materials.

Room control elements

To give all participants the easiest use of the room for any and all presentation or conference purposes, a fully integrated room controller is recommended. It is important that one controller operate all devices in the room so that only one user interface needs to be learned by those managing the facility. The common controller also makes it much easier to expand and enhance room capabilities over time by adding or upgrading equipment. A proper room controller can operate and coordinate the use of lighting, curtains, displays, audio devices, VCRs and slide projectors, as well as all the conferencing equipment, including any network-related control needed. In lieu of a complete control system, a limited functionality controller can be located at the presentation interface panel to control the switching and routing of the computer graphics and configure the overhead camera video paths.

It is strongly advised that at least 20 percent of the time spent developing a videoconferencing room be devoted to this important sub-system, as it will complete the integration of the conference and presentation environment.

And remember that simpler is always better. People do not pay for technology. They pay for the benefits that technology can bring. The doorway to those benefits is a simple, straightforward and intuitive user control.

[1] Davis, Don and Carolyn. "Designing for Intelligibility" in *Handbook for Sound Engineers: The New Audio Cyclopedia*, ed. Glen Ballou (Indianapolis: Howard Sams & Co., 1991), 1279-1297.

A

B

C

T

U

V

Baseband, **9.**4

    Computer, **1.**2

    Digital, **9.**22

    Rf, **9.**5

Video switcher, **9.**14

Viewing

    Area shape, **3.**6

    Distances, **1.**6

White noise, **8.**14

Workstation, **1.**2

XGA, **7.**6

x-height, **2.**3